J. H. Allen
(*M.Sc. Manchester*)

# Chemistry calculations
# for O-level and beyond

THE PROPERTY
OF
READING SCHOOL

| Name | Form |
|------|------|
|      |      |
|      |      |
|      |      |
|      |      |

Nelson

Thomas Nelson and Sons Ltd
Nelson House    Mayfield Road
Walton-on-Thames    Surrey
KT12 5PL    UK

51 York Place
Edinburgh
EH1 3JD    UK

Thomas Nelson (Hong Kong) Ltd
Toppan Building 10/F
22A Westlands Road
Quarry Bay    Hong Kong

Distributed in Australia by

Thomas Nelson Australia
480 La Trobe Street
Melbourne    Victoria 3000
and in Sydney, Brisbane, Adelaide and Perth

First published by Harrap Limited 1983
(under ISBN  0-245-54060-1)

Second impression published by Thomas Nelson and Sons Ltd 1985

ISBN  0-17-444286-6

Print No. 9  8  7  6  5  4  3

Printed in Hong Kong

# Contents

# Preface

This book is intended to provide both guidance and extensive practice in that part of a chemistry course which many candidates find particularly difficult – chemical arithmetic. The material included should be suitable for all Examination Boards and while primarily intended for O-Level some of the questions are of a type which could appear in CSE examination papers.

Each chapter contains several worked examples each of which is followed by questions of a similar type where the required steps are spelt out. In this way it is hoped that plenty of practice will be obtained in the basic ideas. There then follow more general questions where all the previous steps are used but where less help is given.

The arithmetic has been made as simple as possible and in none of the questions should a calculator be required. At the same time examples are worked from first principles and the pupil is not asked to memorise numerous formulae in order to solve the problems.

Some of the later problems are probably beyond the standard of the type of question normally met in an O-Level paper. The same basic ideas are used however and it is felt that there is a place for these to occupy and stimulate those pupils who always work at a faster than average rate. They should also be useful for candidates in the first year of an A-Level course where there is a growing understanding of the subject, and also in new 16+ courses.

# Approximate values for the relative atomic masses of elements

| Aluminium | Al | 27 |
| Antimony | Sb | 122 |
| Arsenic | As | 75 |
| Barium | Ba | 137 |
| Bromine | Br | 80 |
| Calcium | Ca | 40 |
| Carbon | C | 12 |
| Chlorine | Cl | 35.5 |
| Chromium | Cr | 52 |
| Copper | Cu | 64 |
| Fluorine | F | 19 |
| Helium | He | 4 |
| Hydrogen | H | 1 |
| Iodine | I | 127 |
| Iron | Fe | 56 |
| Lead | Pb | 207 |
| Magnesium | Mg | 24 |
| Manganese | Mn | 55 |
| Mercury | Hg | 200 |
| Nickel | Ni | 59 |
| Nitrogen | N | 14 |
| Oxygen | O | 16 |
| Phosphorus | P | 31 |
| Potassium | K | 39 |
| Silicon | Si | 28 |
| Silver | Ag | 108 |
| Sodium | Na | 23 |
| Sulphur | S | 32 |
| Zinc | Zn | 65 |

# Section A
# Relative atomic mass, relative molecular mass and the mole

**Example 1:** Calculate the relative molecular mass of hydrated copper (II) sulphate, $CuSO_4 \cdot 5H_2O$.

$A_r(Cu) = 64$, $A_r(S) = 32$, $A_r(O) = 16$, $A_r(H) = 1$

$$CuSO_4 \cdot 5H_2O$$

$M_r = 64 + 32 + (4 \times 16) + (10 \times 1) + (5 \times 16)$

$\phantom{M_r} = 64 + 32 + 64 + 10 + 80 = \underline{250}$

*Questions:*

1.1. Write down the number of atoms of each element shown in the following formulae:

  (a) $H_2O$

  (b) $CuSO_4$

  (c) $(NH_4)_2SO_4$

  (d) $Al(NO_3)_3$

  (e) $K_4Fe(CN)_6$

  (f) $(NH_4)_2Cr_2O_7$

  (g) $Fe_2(SO_4)_3$

  (h) $MgSO_4 \cdot 7H_2O$

  (i) $Na_2CO_3 \cdot 10H_2O$

1.2. Calculate the relative molecular masses of the following compounds:

  (a) Copper (II) oxide, $CuO$

  (b) Carbon dioxide, $CO_2$

  (c) Sulphuric acid, $H_2SO_4$

  (d) Potassium carbonate, $K_2CO_3$

  (e) Ammonium sulphide, $(NH_4)_2S$

  (f) Calcium phosphate, $Ca_3(PO_4)_2$

  (g) Aluminium sulphate, $Al_2(SO_4)_3$

  (h) Hydrated zinc sulphate, $ZnSO_4 \cdot 7H_2O$

  (i) Lead nitrate, $Pb(NO_3)_2$

  (j) Ammonium iron (II) sulphate, $(NH_4)_2SO_4 \cdot FeSO_4 \cdot 6H_2O$

1

The relative atomic mass of carbon-12, $A_r(C)$, is 12.00. This is used as the standard for all other relative atomic masses.
12.00g of carbon is one mole of carbon.
Similarly, $A_r(O) = 16$, and 16g of oxygen is one mole of oxygen.
$A_r(Fe) = 56$, and 56g of iron is one mole of iron.
All these quantities (12g carbon, 16g oxygen and 56g iron) will contain the same number of atoms – the Avogadro number (L) which is approximately $6 \times 10^{23}$.
The relative molecular mass of the compound water is 18.18g of water is one mole of water and will contain L water molecules.
For magnesium sulphate $M_r(MgSO_4) = 120$. 120g of magnesium sulphate is one mole of magnesium sulphate and will contain L magnesium ions (1 mole of magnesium ions) and L sulphate ions (1 mole of sulphate ions).
For sodium carbonate $M_r(Na_2CO_3) = 106$. 106g of sodium carbonate is one mole of sodium carbonate and will contain 2L sodium ions (2 moles of sodium ions) and L carbonate ions (1 mole of carbonate ions).

---

**Example 2:**   The relative atomic mass of carbon, $A_r(C) = 12$.
    1 mole of carbon = 12g
    $\frac{1}{2}$ mole of carbon = 6g
    0.125 mole of carbon = 1.5g

    12g of carbon = 1 mole
    3g of carbon = $\frac{1}{4}$ mole
    18g of carbon = $1\frac{1}{2}$ moles
    120g of carbon = 10 moles

*Questions:*
2.1.  The relative atomic mass of magnesium is 24. Write down the mass of magnesium represented by
    (a)  1 mole,
    (b)  $\frac{1}{2}$ mole,
    (c)  0.1 mole,
    (d)  2 moles,
    (e)  $3\frac{1}{3}$ moles,
    (f)  0.25 mole,
    (g)  0.04 mole,
    (h)  $x$ moles of magnesium.
2.2.  Write an expression which relates the mass of an element to

2

the number of moles of the element and its relative atomic mass.

2.3. The relative atomic mass of calcium is 40. Write down the number of moles represented by
   (a) 40g,
   (b) 10g,
   (c) 24g,
   (d) 60g,
   (e) 2g,
   (f) 0.12g,
   (g) 170g,
   (h) $x$ g of calcium.

2.4. Write an expression which shows the relation between the number of moles of an element and the mass of the element and its relative atomic mass.

2.5. Write down the mass of the element represented by
   (a) $\frac{1}{3}$ mole of aluminium
   (b) 1.2 moles of carbon
   (c) $3\frac{1}{3}$ moles of potassium
   (d) $\frac{2}{7}$ mole of iron
   (e) 0.04 mole of lead
   (f) $2\frac{1}{2}$ moles of chromium
   (g) 1/200 mole of zinc
   (h) 0.015 mole of sodium

2.6. Find the number of moles of the element represented by
   (a) 9g of carbon
   (b) 13g of zinc
   (c) 23g of lead
   (d) 100g of sulphur
   (e) 24g of iron
   (f) 2g of mercury
   (g) 1.2g of silver
   (h) 0.16g of copper

---

**Example 3:**   Ammonium carbonate, $(NH_4)_2CO_3$
Relative molecular mass, $M_r = 28 + 8 + 12 + 48 = 96$

   96g of ammonium carbonate = 1 mole
   12g of ammonium carbonate = $\frac{1}{8}$ mole
   0.24g of ammonium carbonate = 0.24/96 = 1/400 mole

3

1 mole of ammonium carbonate = 96g

$\frac{2}{3}$ mole of ammonium carbonate = $\frac{2}{3}$ × 96 = 64g

$1\frac{1}{4}$ moles of ammonium carbonate = $\frac{5}{4}$ × 96 = 120g

*Questions:*

3.1. Find the relative molecular mass of magnesium sulphate, $MgSO_4$, and hence the number of moles represented by
   (a) 120g,
   (b) 60g,
   (c) 15g,
   (d) 300g,
   (e) 6g,
   (f) 1.2g,
   (g) 0.3g,
   (h) $x$ g of magnesium sulphate.

3.2. Find the relative molecular mass of copper (II) sulphate $(CuSO_4)$ and hence find the mass of
   (a) 1 mole,
   (b) $\frac{1}{4}$ mole,
   (c) 0.1 mole,
   (d) $3\frac{1}{8}$ mole,
   (e) 0.025 mole,
   (f) 1/200 mole,
   (g) 1.25 mole,
   (h) $x$ moles of copper (II) sulphate.

3.3. Calculate the number of moles represented by the following masses:
   (a) 15g of calcium carbonate, $CaCO_3$
   (b) 8g of ammonium carbonate, $(NH_4)_2CO_3$
   (c) 37g of magnesium nitrate, $Mg(NO_3)_2$
   (d) 40g of iron (III) sulphate, $Fe_2(SO_4)_3$
   (e) 200g of iron (III) oxide, $Fe_2O_3$
   (f) 0.53g of sodium carbonate, $Na_2CO_3$
   (g) 17.1g of aluminium sulphate, $Al_2(SO_4)_3$
   (h) 405g of calcium hydrogen carbonate, $Ca(HCO_3)_2$
   (i) 5g of hydrated copper (II) sulphate, $CuSO_4·5H_2O$
   (j) 4g of gaseous oxygen, $O_2$

3.4. Find the mass of each of the following quantities:
   (a) $\frac{1}{2}$ mole of zinc sulphate, $ZnSO_4$
   (b) $\frac{1}{5}$ mole of aluminium sulphide, $Al_2S_3$
   (c) $1\frac{1}{2}$ moles of copper (II) nitrate, $Cu(NO_3)_2$
   (d) 0.15 moles of magnesium carbonate, $MgCO_3$

4

(e) 0.02 mole of lead nitrate, $Pb(NO_3)_2$

(f) 3.2 moles of iron pyrites, $FeS_2$

(g) 6 moles of gaseous nitrogen, $N_2$

(h) 0.025 mole of hydrated sodium carbonate, $Na_2CO_3 \cdot 10H_2O$

(i) 1/200 mole of hydrated magnesium sulphate, $MgSO_4 \cdot 7H_2O$

---

**Example 4:** It is required to weigh out equal numbers of atoms of iron and sulphur. If 7g of iron is used what mass of sulphur is needed?

In order to obtain equal numbers of atoms of the two elements we must take equal numbers of moles.

56g of iron = 1 mole

7g of iron = $\frac{7}{56}$ = $\frac{1}{8}$ mole

∴ $\frac{1}{8}$ mole of sulphur is needed.

1 mole of sulphur = 32g

∴ $\frac{1}{8}$ mole of sulphur = $\frac{32}{8}$ = <u>4g</u>

*Questions:*

4.1. Calculate the mass of copper which will contain the same number of atoms as there are in

    (a) 2g of sulphur,

    (b) 20g of magnesium,

    (c) 30g of carbon,

    (d) 1g of calcium,

    (e) 78g of zinc,

    (f) 0.5g of mercury.

4.2. Find the mass of

    (a) potassium which contains the same number of atoms as 5g of zinc;

    (b) magnesium which contains the same number of atoms as 40g of sulphur;

    (c) iron which contains the same number of atoms as 75g of mercury;

    (d) carbon which contains the same number of atoms as 130g of chromium.

**Example 5:** How many moles of lead ions and of nitrate ions are contained in $\frac{1}{4}$ mole of lead nitrate?

From the formula $Pb(NO_3)_2$ 1 mole of lead nitrate will contain 1 mole of lead ions and 2 moles of nitrate ions.

$\frac{1}{4}$ mole of lead nitrate will contain $\frac{1}{4}$ mole of lead ions and $\frac{1}{2}$ mole of nitrate ions.

*Questions:*

5.1. Write down the number of moles of each ion in each of the following quantities:
   (a) 0.15 mole of calcium carbonate, $CaCO_3$
   (b) $2\frac{1}{2}$ moles of ammonium sulphate, $(NH_4)_2SO_4$
   (c) $\frac{1}{6}$ mole of calcium phosphate, $Ca_3(PO_4)_2$

5.2. Calculate the number of moles of the compound and of each ion represented by each of the following quantities:
   (a) 47g of silver bromide, $AgBr$
   (b) 5.2g of barium chloride, $BaCl_2$
   (c) 5.13g of aluminium sulphate, $Al_2(SO_4)_3$

*General questions*

6. Calculate the number of moles represented by:
   (a) 80 cm$^3$ of liquid bromine (density 3.2g cm$^{-3}$)
   (b) a cube of aluminium of side 6 cm (density of aluminium $= 2.7g$ cm$^{-3}$)
   (c) 18 dm$^3$ of gaseous oxygen (density $1\frac{1}{3}$g dm$^{-3}$)

7. Using the densities of the elements given in question 6 calculate the volume (cm$^3$) occupied by:
   (a) 0.5 mole of liquid bromine
   (b) 2 moles of aluminium
   (c) 0.02 mole of gaseous oxygen.

8. In each of the following pairs which quantity contains the greater number of moles and hence the greater number of atoms:
   (a) 14g of iron or 40g of mercury
   (b) 4g of silicon or 4g of sulphur
   (c) 26g of zinc or 24g of copper
   (d) 6g of potassium or 4g of magnesium
   (e) 3g of aluminium or 2.3g of sodium
   (f) 88g of calcium or 54g of magnesium
   (g) 182g of iron or 75g of magnesium
   (h) $\frac{1}{6}$g of calcium or 0.048g of carbon?

9. Which of the following quantities represent the same number

6

of moles: 2g of liquid bromine, 0.2g of methane ($CH_4$), 0.3g of aluminium, 0.4g of gaseous oxygen, $3\frac{1}{3}$g of hydrated copper (II) sulphate ($CuSO_4 \cdot 5H_2O$)?

10. Which quantity contains the greater number of moles of sodium ions, 11.7g of sodium chloride ($NaCl$) or 13.25g of sodium carbonate ($Na_2CO_3$)?

11. Which quantity contains the greater number of moles of sulphate ions, 8.7g of potassium sulphate ($K_2SO_4$) or 8.0g of iron (III) sulphate ($Fe_2(SO_4)_3$)?

12. Which is the greater:
   (a) the number of water molecules in 2g of water,
or (b) the number of sulphur dioxide molecules in 8g of sulphur dioxide?

13. Calculate the masses of (a) gaseous nitrogen, and (b) butane ($C_4H_{10}$) which contain the same number of molecules as there are in 48.4g of carbon dioxide.

14. Place the following in order of magnitude:
   (a) the number of octane molecules in 19g of octane ($C_8H_{18}$),
   (b) the number of magnesium ions in 20g of magnesium sulphate ($MgSO_4$),
   (c) the number of sulphur trioxide molecules in 16g of sulphur trioxide,
   (d) the number of nitrate ions in 8.2g of calcium nitrate ($Ca(NO_3)_2$),
   (e) the number of sugar molecules in 57g of the sugar $C_{12}H_{22}O_{11}$,
   (f) the number of lead atoms in 23g of lead.

# Section B
# Formulae of compounds

---

**Example 1:** A compound contains $\frac{1}{3}$ mole of aluminium combined with $\frac{1}{2}$ mole of sulphur. What is the simplest (empirical) formula of the compound?

$\frac{1}{3}$ mole of aluminium combines with $\frac{1}{2}$ mole sulphur.

Multiplying by 6 we have

2 moles aluminium would combine with 3 moles sulphur.

∴ 2L atoms of aluminium would combine with 3L atoms of sulphur (where L is the Avogadro Number).

∴ 2 atoms of aluminium would combine with 3 atoms of sulphur.

The simplest formula of the compound is $\underline{Al_2S_3}$


*Question 1.*

Find the empirical formulae of the compounds in which the following quantities of elements are combined together:

    (a) 1 mole of calcium and 2 moles of chlorine

    (b) 1 mole of potassium and $\frac{1}{2}$ mole of sulphur

    (c) $\frac{1}{4}$ mole of silver and $\frac{1}{8}$ mole of oxygen

    (d) 1/100 mole of lead and $\frac{1}{50}$ mole of oxygen

    (e) 0.04 mole of phosphorus and 0.2 mole of chlorine

    (f) $\frac{1}{6}$ mole of magnesium and $\frac{1}{9}$ mole of nitrogen

    (g) 0.15 mole of zinc and 0.30 mole of bromine

    (h) 0.1 mole of nitrogen and 0.25 mole of oxygen

    (i) $\frac{1}{4}$ mole of iron and $\frac{1}{3}$ mole of oxygen

    (j) 0.8 mole of manganese and 2.8 moles of oxygen.

---

**Example 2:** A compound is found to contain 0.3g of magnesium combined with 2.0g of bromine. What is the empirical formula of the compound?

0.3g of magnesium combines with 2.0g of bromine.

∴ 0.3/24 moles of magnesium combines with 2.0/80 mole of bromine.

$\frac{1}{80}$ mole of magnesium combines with $\frac{2}{80}$ mole of bromine
∴ 1 mole of magnesium would combine with 2 moles of bromine
∴ 1 atom of magnesium would combine with 2 atoms of bromine
The empirical formula of the compound is $\underline{MgBr_2}$

*Questions*
2.1. Find the empirical formulae of the compounds in which the following quantities of elements are combined together:
  (a) 1 mole of sulphur and 32g of oxygen
  (b) 2g of calcium and 0.1 mole of hydrogen
  (c) 0.1 mole of iron and 24g of bromine
  (d) 3.2g of oxygen and 0.1 mole of manganese
  (e) 18g of aluminium and 1 mole of oxygen
  (f) 1.6g of calcium and 0.08 mole of chlorine.
2.2. Calculate the empirical formulae of the compounds which contain the following masses of elements combined together:
  (a) 6.5g of zinc and 1.6g of oxygen
  (b) 1.4g of iron and 1.6g of sulphur
  (c) 13g of chromium and 6g of oxygen
  (d) 0.28g of nitrogen and 0.64g of oxygen
  (e) 3.1g of phosphorus and 2.4g of oxygen
  (f) 0.2g of hydrogen and 5.0g of arsenic
  (g) 0.25g of calcium and 0.15g of carbon
  (h) 1.27g of iodine and 0.4g of oxygen
  (i) 2.1g of silicon and 5.7g of fluorine
  (j) 3.45g of sodium and 1.55g of phosphorus.

---

**Example 3:** 2.88g of an oxide of copper is found to contain 2.56g of copper. What is the empirical formula of the oxide?
Mass of oxygen present = 2.88 − 2.56 = 0.32g
∴ 2.56g of copper combines with 0.32g of oxygen
∴ 2.56/64 mole of copper combines with 0.32/16 mole of oxygen
0.04 mole of copper combines with 0.02 mole of oxygen
∴ 2 moles of copper would combine with 1 mole of oxygen
∴ 2 atoms of copper would combine with 1 atom of oxygen
∴ The empirical formula of the oxide is $\underline{Cu_2O}$

*Question 3.*
(a) 3.30g of a compound of potassium and sulphur is found to

9

contain 2.34g of potassium. What is the empirical formula of the compound?

(b) When 1.8g of aluminium was heated in chlorine until no further reaction occurred 8.9g of aluminium chloride was obtained. Find the empirical formula of the aluminium chloride.

(c) When 13.7g of an oxide of lead was completely reduced 12.42g of lead was obtained. What is the empirical formula of the oxide?

---

**Example 4:** A compound has the empirical formula $NO_2$ and its molar mass is found to be 92g. What is the molecular formula of the compound?

The empirical formula ($NO_2$) shows that the nitrogen and oxygen atoms are present in the ratio of 1:2. The molecular formula is therefore $(NO_2)_x$.

∴ Relative molecular mass $= (14 + 32)x = 46x = 92$

∴ $x = 2$

∴ The molecular formula is $\underline{N_2O_4}$

*Question 4.*

Find (i) the empirical formulae, and (ii) the molecular formulae of the following compounds:

(a) in a compound of molar mass 267g, 3.0g of aluminium is combined with $\frac{1}{3}$ mole of chlorine.

(b) 0.72g of carbon combines with 0.12g of hydrogen to form a compound with a molar mass of 56g.

(c) 3.55g of an oxide of phosphorus is found to contain 1.55g of phosphorus. The molar mass of the compound is 284g.

---

**Example 5:** A compound has the following composition: 52.17% carbon, 13.04% hydrogen and 34.78% oxygen. What is its empirical formula?

|  | % by weight | Relative number of moles | Ratio of moles (atoms) |
|---|---|---|---|
| Carbon | 52.17 | $52.17/12 = 4.35$ | 2 |
| Hydrogen | 13.04 | $13.04/1 = 13.04$ | 6 |
| Oxygen | 34.78 | $34.78/16 = 2.175$ | 1 |

The empirical formula is $\underline{C_2H_6O}$

*Question 5.*
Calculate the empirical formulae of the compounds which have the following compositions:
(a) carbon, 40.00%; hydrogen, 6.67%; oxygen, 53.33%.
(b) carbon, 61.02%; hydrogen, 15.25%; nitrogen, 23.73%.
(c) potassium, 42.39%; iron, 15.22%; carbon, 19.57%; nitrogen, 22.83%.
(d) sodium, 29.11%; sulphur, 40.51%; oxygen, 30.38%.

---

**Example 6:** 1.61g of hydrated sodium sulphate crystals ($Na_2SO_4 \cdot xH_2O$) was heated until no further loss in mass occurred, when 0.71g of the anhydrous salt was obtained. Calculate the formula of the hydrated salt.

$M_r(Na_2SO_4) = 46 + 32 + 64 = 142$
$M_r(H_2O) = 2 + 16 = 18$
Mass of hydrated crystals $= 1.61g$
Mass of anhydrous salt $= 0.71g$
∴ Mass of water $= 0.90g$
0.71g of anhydrous sodium sulphate combines with 0.9g of water.
∴ 0.71/142 mole of anhydrous sodium sulphate combines with 0.9/18 mole of water.
∴ $\frac{1}{200}$ mole of anhydrous sodium sulphate combines with $\frac{1}{20}$ mole of water.
∴ 1 mole of anhydrous sodium sulphate combines with 10 moles of water.
∴ The formula of the hydrated salt is $\underline{Na_2SO_4 \cdot 10H_2O}$

*Question 6.*
In each case, find
(i) the mass of water and of anhydrous compound formed,
(ii) the relative molecular mass of the anhydrous compound,
(iii) the formula of the hydrated compound.
(a) 10.00g of hydrated copper (II) sulphate ($CuSO_4 \cdot xH_2O$) produced 6.4g of the anhydrous salt.
(b) 4.10g of hydrated magnesium sulphate ($MgSO_4 \cdot yH_2O$) gave 2.00g of the anhydrous salt.
(c) 7.3g of hydrated calcium chloride ($CaCl_2 \cdot zH_2O$) gave 3.7g of the anhydrous salt.
(d) 5.04g of hydrated oxalic acid ($H_2C_2O_4 \cdot aH_2O$) gave off 1.44g of water and left the anhydrous acid.

11

**Example 7:** Calculate the percentage by mass of (i) sodium, and (ii) water, in hydrated sodium carbonate, $Na_2CO_3 \cdot 10H_2O$.

Molar mass of $Na_2CO_3 \cdot 10H_2O$
= 46 + 12 + 48 + 180
= 286g

(i) 286g of the compound contains 46g of sodium.

∴ % of sodium in the compound = (46/286) × 100
= 16.08%

(ii) Similarly,

% of water in the hydrated compound = (180/286) × 100
= 62.94%

*Question 7.*

Calculate the percentage by mass of

(a) magnesium in magnesium oxide, $MgO$;
(b) calcium in calcium hydrogen carbonate, $Ca(HCO_3)_2$;
(c) oxygen in lead (II) nitrate, $Pb(NO_3)_2$;
(d) nitrogen in ammonium nitrate, $NH_4NO_3$;
(e) water in hydrated copper (II) sulphate, $CuSO_4 \cdot 5H_2O$.

*General questions*

8. Find the value of x in the formula $FeSO_4 \cdot xH_2O$ for hydrated iron (II) sulphate from the following results obtained by heating the hydrated salt gently until no further change in mass occurred.

Mass of dish = 16.26g
Mass of dish + hydrated crystals = 27.38g
Mass of dish + anhydrous salt = 22.34g.

9. An organic compound had the following composition: carbon, 54.55%; hydrogen, 9.09%; oxygen, 36.36%. The molar mass of the compound was found to be 88g. Calculate the molecular formula of the organic compound.

10. (a) Calculate the percentage by mass of phosphorus in the compound calcium hydrogen phosphate, $Ca(H_2PO_4)_2$.

(b) This compound is contained with other compounds which do not contain phosphorus in a 'general' fertilizer. If the percentage of phosphorus in the fertilizer is given as 5.3%, what fraction of the fertilizer is calcium hydrogen phosphate?

11. The element chromium (Cr) forms two oxides. In oxide *A* 3.9g of chromium is combined with 3.6g of oxygen, while in

oxide *B* 3.9g of chromium is combined with 1.8g of oxygen. Deduce the empirical formulae of the two oxides.

When oxide *A* is strongly heated it decomposes into oxide *B* and oxygen. Write a balanced equation for this reaction, using the formulae you have found for the two oxides.

12. 8.7g of an oxide of iron was heated and a stream of hydrogen was passed over it until no further decrease in mass occurred. At the end of the experiment 6.3g of iron was left. What was the empirical formula of the iron oxide?

Write a balanced equation for the reduction of this oxide by hydrogen.

13. The metal nickel (molar mass = 59g) combines with carbon monoxide to form the compound nickel carbonyl, $Ni(CO)_x$. When 2.95g of nickel was warmed gently in carbon monoxide it was converted completely into 8.55g of nickel carbonyl. Find the mass of carbon monoxide which had combined with the 2.95g of nickel and then deduce the value of x in the formula $Ni(CO)_x$.

14. 1g of mercury was heated in excess chlorine and 1.355g of a chloride of mercury was formed. What is the empirical formula of the chloride?

When this chloride was heated with more mercury, 0.1 mole of it was found to combine with 20g of mercury to form a second chloride. What is the empirical formula of this second chloride of mercury?

The molar mass of the second chloride is 471g. What is its molecular formula?

15. Crystals of hydrated sodium carbonate, $Na_2CO_3 \cdot xH_2O$, contain 37.06% of sodium carbonate, the remainder being water. Calculate the value of x from this information.

Using this value of x find the molar mass of the compound. When left in air for some time 14.3g of the crystals are found to lose 8.1g of water and form a white powder which has the formula $Na_2CO_3 \cdot yH_2O$. Calculate the value of y.

16. The metal manganese forms an oxide in which 0.05 mole of manganese is combined with 1.6g of oxygen. What is the empirical formula of this oxide?

When this oxide was heated with powdered aluminium it was reduced to manganese and an oxide of aluminium was formed. 1.7g of the aluminium oxide was found to contain 0.9g of aluminium. What is the empirical formula of the aluminium oxide?

Assuming that the empirical formulae you have found are also the molecular formulae, write a balanced equation for the reduction of the manganese oxide by aluminium.

17. When a hydrocarbon, $X$, is heated with a suitable catalyst 1 mole of it is converted into 1 mole of a second hydrocarbon, $Y$, and 2 moles of a third hydrocarbon, $Z$.

i.e. $X \longrightarrow Y + 2Z$

Compound $Y$ contains 84.0% by mass of carbon. Find its empirical formula (which is also its molecular formula).

In compound $Z$ 0.3g of carbon is combined with 0.05g of hydrogen. The molar mass of $Z$ is 42g. Find the molecular formula of $Z$.

Deduce the molecular formula of compound $X$.

# Section C
# Calculation of reacting masses from chemical equations

The mass of a substance $C$ which is obtained in a chemical change from a given mass of a substance $A$ may be calculated by using the following steps:

Equation for the chemical change:     $A$  +  $B$ ⟶ $C$  +  $D$

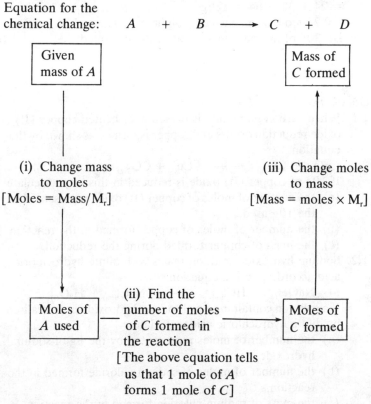

Given mass of $A$

Mass of $C$ formed

(i) Change mass to moles
[Moles = Mass/$M_r$]

(iii) Change moles to mass
[Mass = moles × $M_r$]

Moles of $A$ used

(ii) Find the number of moles of $C$ formed in the reaction
[The above equation tells us that 1 mole of $A$ forms 1 mole of $C$]

Moles of $C$ formed

---

**Example 1:**   10g of magnesium oxide was dissolved completely in dilute sulphuric acid. What mass of magnesium sulphate was formed in the reaction?

The equation for the reaction is

$$MgO_{(s)} + H_2SO_{4(aq)} \longrightarrow MgSO_{4(aq)} + H_2O_{(l)}$$

(i) The molar mass of magnesium oxide, M(MgO),

$= 24 + 16 = 40g$

∴ 10g of magnesium oxide $= \frac{10}{40} = \underline{0.25 \text{ mole}}$

(ii) From the equation,

1 mole of magnesium oxide will form 1 mole of magnesium sulphate

∴ 0.25 mole of magnesium oxide will form $\underline{0.25 \text{ mole of}}$ magnesium sulphate

(iii) The molar mass of magnesium sulphate, M(MgSO$_4$),

$= 24 + 32 + 64 = 120g$

∴ 0.25 mole of magnesium sulphate $= 0.25 \times 120 = 30g$

i.e. 30g of magnesium sulphate will be formed.

*Questions*

1.1. When carbon monoxide is passed over heated copper (II) oxide reduction occurs and copper is formed as shown by the equation

$$CuO_{(s)} + CO_{(g)} \longrightarrow Cu_{(s)} + CO_{2(g)}$$

If 10g of copper (II) oxide is reduced in this way, calculate

(a) the number of moles of copper (II) oxide represented by the 10g used,

(b) the number of moles of copper formed in the reaction,

(c) the mass of copper formed during the reduction.

1.2. Sodium hydroxide solution reacts with dilute hydrochloric acid according to the equation

$$NaOH_{(aq)} + HCl_{(aq)} \longrightarrow NaCl_{(aq)} + H_2O_{(l)}$$

If a solution containing 8g of sodium hydroxide is neutralised by dilute hydrochloric acid, calculate

(a) the number of moles represented by the 8g of sodium hydroxide,

(b) the number of moles of sodium chloride formed in the reaction,

(c) the mass of sodium chloride formed in the reaction.

1.3. When aqueous solutions of copper (II) sulphate and sodium carbonate are mixed a green precipitate of copper (II) carbonate is formed:

$$CuSO_{4(aq)} + Na_2CO_{3(aq)} \longrightarrow CuCO_{3(s)} + Na_2SO_{4(aq)}$$

16

If 8g of copper (II) sulphate are reacted with sodium carbonate, calculate,
- (a) the number of moles represented by the 8g of copper (II) sulphate,
- (b) the number of moles of copper (II) carbonate formed during the reaction,
- (c) the mass of copper (II) carbonate formed.

1.4. Zinc carbonate reacts with dilute sulphuric acid as follows:

$$ZnCO_{3(s)} + H_2SO_{4(aq)} \longrightarrow$$
$$ZnSO_{4(aq)} + CO_{2(g)} + H_2O_{(l)}$$

If 2.5g of zinc carbonate are dissolved in dilute sulphuric acid, calculate,
- (a) the number of moles of zinc carbonate which are dissolved,
- (b) the number of moles of carbon dioxide given off during the reaction,
- (c) the mass of carbon dioxide formed in the reaction.

1.5. When aqueous solutions of ammonium sulphate and barium chloride are added together a white precipitate of barium sulphate is formed:

$$(NH_4)_2SO_{4(aq)} + BaCl_{2(aq)} \longrightarrow$$
$$BaSO_{4(s)} + 2NH_4Cl_{(aq)}$$

If barium chloride solution is added to a solution containing 11g of ammonium sulphate, calculate
- (a) the number of moles of ammonium sulphate used,
- (b) the number of moles of barium sulphate formed in the reaction,
- (c) the mass of barium sulphate formed.

---

**Example 2:** When iron pyrites ($FeS_2$) is roasted in oxygen it is converted into iron (III) oxide and sulphur dioxide is formed:

$$4FeS_{2(s)} + 11O_{2(g)} \longrightarrow 2Fe_2O_{3(s)} + 8SO_{2(g)}$$

Calculate the mass of oxygen required to react completely with 30g of iron pyrites.

(i) The molar mass of iron pyrites, $M(FeS_2) = 56 + 64 = 120g$
30g of iron pyrites $= 30/120 = \frac{1}{4}$ mole
(ii) From the equation,
4 moles of iron pyrites react with 11 moles of oxygen
1 mole of iron pyrites reacts with 11/4 moles of oxygen
$\frac{1}{4}$ mole of iron pyrites reacts with $(11/4) \times (1/4) = 11/16$ mole of oxygen
(iii) The molar mass of oxygen, $M(O_2) = 32g$

11/16 mole of oxygen = $11/16 \times 32$ = 22g
22g of oxygen are required for the reaction.

*Questions*

2.1. Gaseous ammonia reacts with heated copper (II) oxide according to the equation:
$$3CuO_{(s)} + 2NH_{3(g)} \longrightarrow 3Cu_{(s)} + N_{2(g)} + 3H_2O_{(l)}$$
In an experiment, 1.7g of ammonia was passed over heated copper (II) oxide. Calculate
  (a) the number of moles of ammonia used,
  (b) the number of moles of nitrogen formed,
  (c) the mass of nitrogen formed in the reaction.

2.2. When sodium hydrogen carbonate is added to dilute sulphuric acid the reaction can be represented by the equation:
$$2NaHCO_{3(s)} + H_2SO_{4(aq)} \longrightarrow$$
$$Na_2SO_{4(aq)} + 2CO_{2(g)} + 2H_2O_{(l)}$$
If 2.1g of sodium hydrogen carbonate is added to the acid, calculate
  (a) the number of moles of sodium hydrogen carbonate which are added,
  (b) the number of moles of carbon dioxide formed,
  (c) the mass of carbon dioxide formed in the reaction,
  (d) the volume of carbon dioxide formed, given that 1 mole of carbon dioxide occupies 24 dm$^3$ under the conditions of the experiment.

2.3. Iron (III) oxide is reduced by carbon monoxide according to the equation:
$$Fe_2O_{3(s)} + 3CO_{(g)} \longrightarrow 2Fe_{(s)} + 3CO_{2(g)}$$
It is required to make 7g of iron by this reaction. Find
  (a) the number of moles represented by this 7g of iron,
  (b) the number of moles of iron (III) oxide needed to produce this quantity of iron,
  (c) the mass of iron (III) oxide required.

2.4. Aqueous solutions of sodium hydroxide and magnesium chloride react to form a white precipitate of magnesium hydroxide:
$$2NaOH_{(aq)} + MgCl_{2(aq)} \longrightarrow$$
$$Mg(OH)_{2(s)} + 2NaCl_{(aq)}$$
3.8g of magnesium chloride are dissolved in water and aqueous sodium hydroxide is added until the reaction is complete. Calculate
  (a) the number of moles of magnesium chloride dissolved,

18

(b) the number of moles of sodium hydroxide required for complete reaction,

(c) the mass of sodium hydroxide which is needed for the reaction.

2.5. Aqueous solutions of iron (III) sulphate and barium chloride react according to the following equation:

$$Fe_2(SO_4)_{3(aq)} + 3BaCl_{2(aq)} \longrightarrow$$
$$3BaSO_{4(s)} + 2FeCl_{3(aq)}$$

6.99g of barium sulphate are obtained as a result of the above reaction. Calculate

(a) the number of moles of barium sulphate represented by the 6.99g,

(b) the number of moles of iron (III) sulphate and of barium chloride which will react together to produce this quantity of barium sulphate,

(c) the masses of iron (III) sulphate and of barium chloride which have reacted together.

2.6. Methane $(CH_4)$ is produced by the reaction of aluminium carbide and water according to the equation:

$$Al_4C_{3(s)} + 12H_2O_{(l)} \longrightarrow 4Al(OH)_{3(s)} + 3CH_{4(g)}$$

If 60 $dm^3$ of methane have to be prepared and if 1 mole of methane occupies 24 $dm^3$ under the conditions of the experiment, calculate

(a) the number of moles of methane which are required,

(b) the number of moles of aluminium carbide which will be needed to produce this quantity of methane,

(c) the mass of aluminium carbide required for the reaction.

---

**Example 3:** A solution of the chloride of a divalent metal $X$ reacts with aqueous silver nitrate according to the equation:

$$XCl_{2(aq)} + 2AgNO_{3(aq)} \longrightarrow 2AgCl_{(s)} + X(NO_3)_{2(aq)}$$

In an experiment to determine the relative atomic mass of $X$ 1.8g of its chloride were dissolved in water and excess silver nitrate solution was added. The precipitate of silver chloride formed was found to weigh 4.1g. What value does this give for $A_r(X)$?

(i) $M(AgCl) = 108 + 35.5 = 143.5$

$\therefore$ 4.1g of silver chloride = 4.1/143.5 = 2/70 mole

(ii) From the equation,

2 moles of silver chloride are formed from 1 mole of $XCl_2$

$\therefore$ 2/70 mole of silver chloride is formed from 1/70 mole of $XCl_2$

19

(iii) 1/70 mole of $XCl_2$ must be represented by 1.8g of $XCl_2$

∴ 1 mole is represented by $70 \times 1.8 = \underline{126g}$

(iv) $M(XCl_2) = A(X) + 71 = 126g$

∴ $A(X) = 126 - 71 = 55g$

i.e. the relative atomic mass of the metal $X = \underline{55}$

*Questions*

3.1. 0.8g of the oxide of a metal $Z$ reacts exactly with 0.02 mole of aqueous hydrochloric acid according to the equation:

$$ZO_{(s)} + 2HCl_{(aq)} \longrightarrow ZCl_{2(aq)} + H_2O_{(l)}$$

Calculate

(a) the number of moles of the oxide which would react with the 0.02 mole of hydrochloric acid,

(b) the molar mass of ZO and hence the relative atomic mass of Z.

3.2. When 3.48g of the sulphate of a metal $R$ was dissolved in water and excess barium chloride solution was added the precipitate of barium sulphate formed had a mass of 4.66g. The reaction which occurred is represented by the equation:

$$R_2SO_{4(aq)} + BaCl_{2(aq)} \longrightarrow BaSO_{4(s)} + 2RCl_{(aq)}$$

Calculate

(a) the number of moles of barium sulphate formed,

(b) the number of moles of $R_2SO_4$ needed to produce this quantity of barium sulphate,

(c) the value of $M(R_2SO_4)$ and of $A_r(R)$.

3.3. 5.1g of the oxide of a trivalent metal $Q$ is found to require 14.7g of aqueous sulphuric acid for complete reaction according to the equation:

$$Q_2O_{3(s)} + 3H_2SO_{4(aq)} \longrightarrow Q_2(SO_4)_{3(aq)} + 3H_2O_{(l)}$$

Calculate

(a) the number of moles represented by the 14.7g of sulphuric acid,

(b) the number of moles of the oxide with which this acid would react,

(c) the molar mass of the oxide and hence the relative atomic mass of $Q$.

3.4. 2.4g of sodium hydroxide was dissolved in water and added to a solution containing a sulphate $X_2(SO_4)_3$, when a precipitate of the hydroxide of the metal $X$ was formed:

$$X_2(SO_4)_{3(aq)} + 6NaOH_{(aq)} \longrightarrow$$
$$2X(OH)_{3(s)} + 3Na_2SO_{4(aq)}$$

The precipitate was filtered, washed, dried and heated to constant mass when 1.6g of the oxide $X_2O_3$ was obtained:
$$2X(OH)_{3(s)} \longrightarrow X_2O_{3(s)} + 3H_2O_{(l)}$$
Calculate
(a) the number of moles of sodium hydroxide which were dissolved,
(b) using the two equations, the number of moles of the oxide $X_2O_3$ which would be formed,
(c) the molar mass of this oxide and hence the relative atomic mass of $X$.

*General questions*
4. This question refers to the reaction of magnesium oxide with aqueous sulphuric acid:
$$MgO_{(s)} + H_2SO_{4(aq)} \longrightarrow MgSO_{4(aq)} + H_2O_{(l)}$$
Find the values of
(a) $M(MgO)$,
(b) $M(H_2SO_4)$,
(c) $M(MgSO_4)$.
Copy out the following table and complete the spaces indicated.

| Mass of MgO used | No. of moles of MgO used | No. of moles of $H_2SO_4$ used | Mass of $H_2SO_4$ used | No. of moles of $MgSO_4$ formed | Mass of $MgSO_4$ formed |
|---|---|---|---|---|---|
|  | 0.5 | ? | ? |  |  |
| 1.0g | ? | ? | ? |  |  |
| 30g | ? |  |  | ? | ? |
| ? | ? | ? | 4.9g |  |  |
| ? | ? | ? | ? | ? | 15g |

5. This question refers to the reaction between steam and strongly heated iron:
$$3Fe_{(s)} + 4H_2O_{(g)} \longrightarrow Fe_3O_{4(s)} + 4H_{2(g)}$$
What are the values of
(a) $M(Fe)$,
(b) $M(Fe_3O_4)$,
(c) $M(H_2)$?

Copy out the following table and complete where indicated:

| Mass of iron used | No. of moles of iron used | No. of moles of iron oxide formed | Mass of iron oxide formed | No. of moles of hydrogen formed | Mass of hydrogen formed |
|---|---|---|---|---|---|
| 42g | ? | ? | ? | | |
| ? | 0.3 | ? | ? | | |
| 6.3g | ? | | | ? | ? |
| ? | ? | ? | 11.6g | | |
| ? | ? | ? | ? | ? | 1.0g |

6. When iron pyrites ($FeS_2$) is roasted in air it reacts according to the equation:

$$4FeS_{2(s)} + 11O_{2(g)} \longrightarrow 2Fe_2O_{3(s)} + 8SO_{2(g)}$$

It is required to make 4 000 Kg of sulphur dioxide by this reaction.

What mass of iron pyrites will have to be used, assuming complete reaction according to the above equation?

If all the sulphur dioxide is then converted into sulphuric acid what is the mass of acid which is obtained?

7. 1.8g of magnesium was added to a dilute solution of sulphuric acid containing 4.9g of the acid. At the end of the reaction there was some magnesium unreacted. Calculate the mass of magnesium left.

What mass of acid would have been required to react with all the 1.8g of magnesium?

8. 5.41g of the hydrated chloride $XCl_3 \cdot 6H_2O$ was dissolved in water and excess silver nitrate solution was added. The precipitated silver chloride had a mass of 8.61g.

Write the equation for the reaction and calculate the molar mass of the hydrated chloride and the relative atomic mass of the metal $X$.

9. Hard water containing calcium compounds may be softened by adding sodium carbonate, when calcium carbonate is precipitated.

A reservoir contains 100 000 $M^3$ of water and the water contains 1.7g $M^{-3}$ of calcium sulphate. Calculate the mass of sodium carbonate ($Na_2CO_3$) required to soften all the water in the reservoir completely.

What will be the total mass of calcium carbonate precipitated during the softening process?

10. 10g of a mixture containing hydrated sodium sulphate ($Na_2SO_4 \cdot 10H_2O$) and sodium chloride is dissolved in water and an aqueous solution of barium chloride is added until the reaction is complete. The barium sulphate formed is filtered off, washed and dried, and is found to weigh 4.66g. Calculate the percentage of hydrated sodium sulphate in the original mixture.

What will be the total mass of sodium chloride left in the solution after the above reaction has taken place?

11. (a) Basic lead (II) carbonate may be represented by the formula $Pb(OH)_2 \cdot 2PbCO_3$ and when heated it is converted into lead (II) oxide. Calculate the mass of lead (II) oxide which can be obtained by heating 31g of the basic carbonate.

(b) Lead (II) oxide is also formed, together with oxygen, when red lead ($Pb_3O_4$) is heated. What mass of red lead will have to be heated in order to obtain the same mass of lead (II) oxide as that formed in (a)?

12. 10g of copper was warmed with 150 cm$^3$ of dilute nitric acid. When the reaction had finished excess copper was filtered off, the copper (II) nitrate solution was evaporated carefully and the solid nitrate was then heated gently to yield 10g of copper (II) oxide.

Assuming that the reaction of the copper and acid may be represented by the equation:

$$3Cu_{(s)} + 8HNO_{3(aq)} \longrightarrow 3Cu(NO_3)_{2(aq)} + 4H_2O_{(l)} + 2NO_{(g)}$$

calculate (a) the mass of copper which had not reacted, and
(b) the concentration of the nitric acid in g dm$^{-3}$.

13. A mixture of sodium hydrogen carbonate and anhydrous sodium carbonate was heated gently until no further loss in mass occurred. During the heating 0.55g of carbon dioxide was formed and when the residue was cooled it was found to weigh 4.225g.

Assuming that all the carbon dioxide was formed from the sodium hydrogen carbonate, calculate (a) the mass of sodium hydrogen carbonate and (b) the percentage of anhydrous sodium carbonate in the original mixture.

23

# Section D
# Concentration of solutions and volumetric analysis

The concentration of a solution is expressed either as moles per $dm^3$ of solution ($mol\ dm^{-3}$) or as grammes per $dm^3$ of solution ($g\ dm^{-3}$).

$(1\ dm^3 = 1000\ cm^3 = 1\ litre)$

The concentration in $mol\ dm^{-3}$ is known as the molarity of the solution. E.g. a solution containing 0.25 moles of solute per $dm^3$ has a molarity of 0.25 M.

---

**Example 1:** How many moles of copper sulphate are contained in 25 $cm^3$ of a solution containing 2 moles of copper sulphate per $dm^3$?

   1 000 $cm^3$ of the solution contain 2 moles

     100 $cm^3$ of the solution contain 0.2 mole

      25 $cm^3$ of the solution contain 0.05 mole of copper sulphate.

---

*Question 1*

Calculate the number of moles of solute in

(a)  20 $cm^3$ of a solution containing 5 $mol\ dm^{-3}$,

(b)  50 $cm^3$ of a solution containing 3 $mol\ dm^{-3}$,

(c)  30 $cm^3$ of a solution containing 1 $mol\ dm^{-3}$,

(d)  40 $cm^3$ of a solution containing 2.5 $mol\ dm^{-3}$,

(e)  24 $cm^3$ of a solution containing 2 $mol\ dm^{-3}$.

---

**Example 2:** 25 $cm^3$ of a solution contains 0.1 mole of sodium hydroxide. What is the concentration of the solution in $mol\ dm^{-3}$?

      25 $cm^3$ of the solution contain 0.1 mole

    100 $cm^3$ of the solution contain 0.4 mole

  1 000 $cm^3$ of the solution contain 4.0 moles

i.e. the concentration of the solution = 4 $mol\ dm^{-3}$.

or the molarity of the solution = 4 M

*Question 2*
Calculate the concentration in mol dm$^{-3}$ (the molarities) of solutions of which
(a) 20 cm$^3$ contain 0.01 mole of solute,
(b) 40 cm$^3$ contain 0.1 mole of solute,
(c) 30 cm$^3$ contain 0.2 mole of solute,
(d) 12.5 cm$^3$ contain 0.05 mole of solute.
(e) 22 cm$^3$ contain 0.033 mole of solute.

---

**Example 3:**   What mass of sodium hydroxide is contained in 25 cm$^3$ of a solution containing 0.5 mol dm$^{-3}$ of sodium hydroxide?
   1 000 cm$^3$ of the solution contain 0.5 mole
     100 cm$^3$ of the solution contain 0.05 mole
       25 cm$^3$ of the solution contain 0.0125 mole of sodium hydroxide.
   But the molar mass, M(NaOH) = 23 + 16 + 1 = 40g
   The mass of sodium hydroxide in 25 cm$^3$ of the solution is
   $0.0125 \times 40 = \underline{0.5g}$

*Question 3*
Calculate the mass of solute in the following volumes of solutions:
(a) 50 cm$^3$ of a solution containing 2 mol dm$^{-3}$ of magnesium sulphate, $MgSO_4$;
(b) 20 cm$^3$ of a solution containing 1.25 mol dm$^{-3}$ of copper sulphate, $CuSO_4$;
(c) 40 cm$^3$ of a solution containing $\frac{1}{10}$ mol dm$^{-3}$ of sodium carbonate, $Na_2CO_3$;
(d) 25 cm$^3$ of a solution containing 0.4 mol dm$^{-3}$ of potassium hydroxide, KOH;
(e) 10 cm$^3$ of a solution containing $\frac{3}{8}$ mol dm$^{-3}$ of iron (III) sulphate, $Fe_2(SO_4)_3$.

---

**Example 4:**   25 cm$^3$ of a solution contains 0.85g of silver nitrate. What is the concentration of the solution in mol dm$^{-3}$?
25 cm$^3$ of solution contain 0.85g of silver nitrate
100 cm$^3$ of solution contain 3.40g of silver nitrate
1 000 cm$^3$ of solution contain 34.0g of silver nitrate
$M(AgNO_3)$ = 108 + 14 + 48 = 170g
The concentration of the solution = $34/170 = \underline{0.2 \text{ mol dm}^{-3}}$
or the molarity of the solution = $\underline{0.2 \text{ M}}$

## Question 4

Calculate the concentration in mol dm$^{-3}$ (the molarities) of solutions of which

(a)  20 cm$^3$ contain 0.6g of magnesium sulphate, $MgSO_4$
(b)  30 cm$^3$ contain 6.0g of sodium hydroxide, $NaOH$
(c)  50 cm$^3$ contain 0.7g of sulphuric acid, $H_2SO_4$
(d)  25 cm$^3$ contain 1.325g of sodium carbonate, $Na_2CO_3$
(e)  18 cm$^3$ contain 3.6g of hydrated copper (II) sulphate, $CuSO_4 \cdot 5H_2O$.

---

**Example 5:**   A solution contains 0.5 mol dm$^{-3}$ of sodium carbonate. What volume of the solution will have to be measured out to obtain 0.01 moles of sodium carbonate?

0.5 moles are contained in 1 000 cm$^3$ of the solution
0.1 moles are contained in 200 cm$^3$ of the solution
0.01 moles are contained in 20 cm$^3$ of the solution.

## Question 5

Calculate the volume of solution required to obtain:

(a)  0.1 mole of potassium hydroxide using a solution containing 2 mol dm$^{-3}$ of potassium hydroxide;
(b)  0.004 mole of silver nitrate using a solution containing 0.1 mol dm$^{-3}$ of silver nitrate;
(c)  0.01 moles of sodium hydroxide using a solution containing 10g dm$^{-3}$ of sodium hydroxide;
(d)  0.015 mole of magnesium sulphate using a solution containing 6g of magnesium sulphate ($MgSO_4$) in 100 cm$^3$ of solution.

---

**Example 6:**   25 cm$^3$ of a solution containing 2 mol dm$^{-3}$ of hydrochloric acid react completely with 20 cm$^3$ of a solution of sodium carbonate. What is the concentration of the sodium carbonate solution in (i) mol dm$^{-3}$, (ii) g dm$^{-3}$?

The equation for the reaction is

$$Na_2CO_{3(aq)} + 2HCl_{(aq)} \longrightarrow 2NaCl_{(aq)} + CO_{2(g)} + H_2O_{(l)}$$

(a)  1 000 cm$^3$ of the hydrochloric acid solution contain 2 moles
100 cm$^3$ of the hydrochloric acid solution contain 0.2 mole
25 cm$^3$ of the hydrochloric acid solution contain 0.05 mole

(b)  From the equation,
2 moles of acid react with 1 mole of sodium carbonate
∴ 0.05 mole of acid react with 0.025 mole of sodium carbonate

(c) The 20 cm$^3$ of sodium carbonate solution must contain 0.025 mole

100 cm$^3$ of sodium carbonate solution will contain 0.125 mole
1 000 cm$^3$ of sodium carbonate solution will contain 1.25 moles

The concentration of the sodium carbonate solution is
<u>1.25 mol dm$^{-3}$</u>

$$M(Na_2CO_3) = 46 + 12 + 48 = 106g$$
∴ The concentration of the solution is $1.25 \times 106 = $ <u>132.5 g dm$^{-3}$</u>.

*Questions*

6.1. In each of the following cases write the equation for the reaction which occurs and find:
  (i) the number of moles used of the first solute,
  (ii) the number of moles of the second solute required for complete reaction,
  (iii) the concentration of the second solution in mol dm$^{-3}$:
  (a) 20 cm$^3$ of a 1.0 mol dm$^{-3}$ (1.0 M) solution of sodium hydroxide neutralises 20 cm$^3$ of hydrochloric acid solution;
  (b) 25 cm$^3$ of an 0.8 mol dm$^{-3}$ (0.8 M) solution of sulphuric acid neutralise 40 cm$^3$ of a solution of potassium hydroxide;
  (c) 20 cm$^3$ of a 3.75 mol dm$^{-3}$ (3.75 M) solution of calcium chloride react exactly with 30 cm$^3$ of a silver nitrate solution;
  (d) 20 cm$^3$ of an 0.05 mol dm$^{-3}$ (0.05 M) solution of nitric acid react exactly with 25 cm$^3$ of sodium carbonate solution;
  (e) 35 cm$^3$ of aqueous sulphuric acid of concentration 14g dm$^{-3}$ neutralise 10 cm$^3$ of an aqueous solution of the compound X(OH)$_3$.

6.2. In the following examples write the equation for the reaction which occurs and find the concentration of the second solution in mol dm$^{-3}$ and hence in g dm$^{-3}$:
  (a) 50 cm$^3$ of 0.1 mol dm$^{-3}$ (0.1 M) hydrochloric acid solution neutralise 20 cm$^3$ of a solution of potassium hydroxide;
  (b) 25 cm$^3$ of 0.96 mol dm$^{-3}$ (0.96 M) nitric acid solution neutralise 30 cm$^3$ of a solution of barium hydroxide;
  (c) 50 cm$^3$ of a solution containing 8.5g dm$^{-3}$ of silver nitrate

react exactly with 10 cm³ of a solution of magnesium bromide;

(d) 37 cm³ containing 1.43g of hydrated sodium carbonate, $Na_2CO_3 \cdot 10H_2O$, react with 25 cm³ of aqueous hydrochloric acid.

---

**Example 7:** What volume of 0.5 M sulphuric acid solution is needed to neutralise 25 cm³ of a 2 M solution of sodium hydroxide?

The equation for the reaction is

$$2NaOH_{(aq)} + H_2SO_{4(aq)} \longrightarrow Na_2SO_{4(aq)} + 2H_2O_{(l)}$$

(a) 1 000 cm³ of the sodium hydroxide solution contain 2 moles
25 cm³ of the sodium hydroxide solution contain <u>0.05 moles</u>

(b) From the equation
2 moles of sodium hydroxide neutralise 1 mole of sulphuric acid
0.05 moles of sodium hydroxide neutralise <u>0.025 mole of acid</u>

(c) 0.5 mole of acid are contained in 1 000 cm³ of the solution
0.25 mole of acid are contained in 500 cm³ of the solution
0.025 mole of acid are contained in 50 cm³ of the solution
<u>50 cm³ of the sulphuric acid solution are required</u>

---

*Question 7*

In each of the following examples of titrations write the equation for the reaction which occurs and calculate

 (i) the number of moles of solute in the given volume of solution,
 (ii) the number of moles of the second reagent needed for complete reaction,
(iii) the volume of the second solution which will be required:

(a) 25 cm³ of aqueous hydrochloric acid of concentration 1 mol $dm^{-3}$ is neutralised by aqueous sodium hydroxide of concentration 1 mol $dm^{-3}$.

(b) 40 cm³ of a 1.0 M solution of hydrochloric acid is neutralised by a 1.0 M aqueous solution of sodium carbonate.

(c) 20 cm³ of an aqueous solution of potassium carbonate of concentration 1 mol $dm^{-3}$ is neutralised by aqueous sulphuric acid of concentration 2 mol $dm^{-3}$.

(d) 10 cm³ of an 0.5 M aqueous solution of ammonium chloride is completely reacted with an 0.02 M aqueous solution of silver nitrate.

28

(e) 50 cm$^3$ of aqueous sodium hydroxide of concentration 5g dm$^{-3}$ is neutralised by an aqueous solution of sulphuric acid of concentration 0.125 mol dm$^{-3}$.

---

**Example 8:** In an experiment to determine the relative atomic mass of a monovalent metal $X$, 50 cm$^3$ of an aqueous solution containing 11.2g of the hydroxide of $X$ was found to neutralise 50 cm$^3$ of aqueous sulphuric acid of concentration 2 mol dm$^{-3}$. What is the relative atomic mass of $X$?

The equation for the reaction is

$$2XOH_{(aq)} + H_2SO_{4(aq)} \longrightarrow X_2SO_{4(aq)} + 2H_2O_{(l)}$$

(a) 1 000 cm$^3$ of the acid solution contain 2 moles of sulphuric acid

100 cm$^3$ of the acid solution contain 0.2 moles of sulphuric acid

50 cm$^3$ of the acid solution contain 0.1 mole of sulphuric acid.

(b) From the equation
1 mole of sulphuric acid reacts with 2 moles of XOH
∴ 0.1 mole of sulphuric acid reacts with 0.2 mole of XOH

(c) 0.2 mole of XOH is represented by 11.2g
∴ 1 mole of XOH is represented by 56.0g
i.e. the molar mass of XOH = 56.0g

(d) $M_r(XOH) = A_r(X) + 16 + 1 = 56$
∴ $A_r(X) = 39$
The relative atomic mass of $X$ is 39.

*Questions*

8.1. The hydroxide of a metal Z reacts with hydrochloric acid according to the following equation:

$$Z(OH)_{2(s)} + 2HCl_{(aq)} \longrightarrow ZCl_{2(aq)} + 2H_2O_{(l)}$$

5.8g of the hydroxide was found to react with 0.2 mole of acid. Find

(a) how many moles of the hydroxide react with the 0.2 mole of hydrochloric acid,

(b) the molar mass of $Z(OH)_2$,

(c) the relative atomic mass of Z.

8.2. In each of the following examples
(i) write the equation for the reaction which occurs,

    (ii)  find the number of moles of acid used,

    (iii)  find the number of moles of the compound of the unknown element $(M, X, A)$ with which the acid reacts,

    (iv)  find the molar mass of the compound and hence the relative atomic mass of the unknown element.

(a)  1.6g of an oxide $MO$ reacts exactly with 20 cm³ of a solution of hydrochloric acid of concentration 2 mol dm⁻³.

(b)  0.34g of the oxide of a metal $X$ (which is in Group 3 of the Periodic Table) reacts completely with 50 cm³ of 0.2M aqueous sulphuric acid.

(c)  50 cm³ of an aqueous solution of a carbonate $A_2CO_3$ of concentration 5.8g dm⁻³ reacts with 50 cm³ of aqueous nitric acid of concentration 0.05 mol dm⁻³.

---

**Example 9:**  2.65g of impure sodium carbonate was dissolved in water and the solution made up to 100 cm³. 25 cm³ of this solution was found to require 20 cm³ of aqueous sulphuric acid of concentration 0.25 mol dm⁻³ for complete reaction. Calculate the percentage purity of the sodium carbonate used.

The equation for the reaction is

$$Na_2CO_{3(aq)} + H_2SO_{4(aq)} \longrightarrow$$
$$Na_2SO_{4(aq)} + CO_{2(g)} + H_2O_{(l)}$$

(a)  1 000 cm³ of the acid solution contain 0.25 mole of the acid
100 cm³ of the acid solution contain 0.025 mole of acid
20 cm³ of the acid solution contain 0.005 mole of acid.

(b)  From the equation
1 mole of sulphuric acid reacts with 1 mole of sodium carbonate
∴ 0.005 mole of sulphuric acid reacts with 0.005 mole of sodium carbonate
∴ 25 cm³ of the sodium carbonate solution contain 0.005 mole
∴ 100 cm³ of the sodium carbonate solution contain 0.02 mole

(c)  $M(Na_2CO_3) = 106g$
∴ 100 cm³ of the sodium carbonate solution contain
$0.02 \times 106 = 2.12g$ of sodium carbonate
∴ 2.65g of the impure sodium carbonate contains 2.12g of sodium carbonate.

∴ The % purity $= \dfrac{2.12}{2.65} \times 100 = \underline{80\%}$

*Question 9*
7.8g of rock salt (impure sodium chloride) was weighed, dissolved in water and the solution made up to 1 $dm^3$. 25 $cm^3$ of this solution was found to react with 50 $cm^3$ of an 0.05M solution of silver nitrate. Write the equation for this reaction and calculate:
(a)  the number of moles of silver nitrate in the 50 $cm^3$ of solution,
(b)  the number of moles of sodium chloride with which this silver nitrate reacts,
(c)  the concentration of the sodium chloride solution in mol $dm^{-3}$ and then in g $dm^{-3}$,
(d)  the percentage by mass of sodium chloride in the rock salt.

---

**Example 10:**   A solution contains 2 mol $dm^{-3}$ of magnesium chloride, $MgCl_2$.
Find the number of moles in 100 $cm^3$ of the solution of:
 (i) magnesium chloride,
 (ii) magnesium ions,
(iii) chloride ions.
1 000 $cm^3$ of the solution contains 2 moles of magnesium chloride.
∴ 100 $cm^3$ of the solution contains 0.2 mole of magnesium chloride.
According to the formula, 1 mole of magnesium chloride will contain 1 mole of magnesium ions and 2 moles of chloride ions.
∴ 100 $cm^3$ of the solution contains 0.2 moles of magnesium ions and 0.4 moles of chloride ions.

*Questions*
10.1. A solution contains 1.2 mol $dm^{-3}$ of hydrated sodium sulphate, $Na_2SO_4 \cdot 10H_2O$. Calculate the number of moles in 50 $cm^3$ of the solution of:
(a) hydrated sodium sulphate,
(b) anhydrous sodium sulphate,
(c) sodium ions,
(d) sulphate ions,
(e) water of crystallisation.
10.2. A solution contains 100g $dm^{-3}$ of iron (III) sulphate, $Fe_2(SO_4)_3$.
Find the number of moles in 500 $cm^3$ of the solution of
(a) iron (III) sulphate,
(b) iron (III) ions,
(c) sulphate ions.

*General questions*

11. The formula of hydrated ethandioic acid (oxalic acid) is $H_2C_2O_4 \cdot xH_2O$. The acid reacts with sodium hydroxide according to the equation:

$$H_2C_2O_{4(aq)} + 2NaOH_{(aq)} \longrightarrow Na_2C_2O_{4(aq)} + 2H_2O_{(l)}$$

6.3g of the hydrated acid was dissolved in 1 dm$^3$ of aqueous solution, and 20 cm$^3$ of this solution was found to neutralise 24 cm$^3$ of a $\frac{1}{12}$ M aqueous sodium hydroxide solution.
Calculate
(a) the number of moles of sodium hydroxide in the 24 cm$^3$ of the solution,
(b) the number of moles of ethandioic acid in the 20 cm$^3$ of the solution (from your answer to (a) and the equation), and hence in 1 dm$^3$ of the solution,
(c) the mass of anhydrous ethandioic acid in 1 dm$^3$ of the solution,
(d) the mass of water in 6.3g of the hydrated ethandioic acid and hence the value of x in the formula $H_2C_2O_4 \cdot xH_2O$.

12. 25 cm$^3$ of 0.01M aqueous phosphoric acid ($H_3PO_4$) neutralises 50 cm$^3$ of 0.01M aqueous sodium hydroxide.
Find
(a) the number of moles of phosphoric acid in the 25 cm$^3$ of solution,
(b) the number of moles of sodium hydroxide in the 50 cm$^3$ of solution.
By using your answers to (a) and (b) deduce the formula of the salt formed and write the equation for the reaction which occurs.

13. In what proportions by volume will solutions containing respectively 2.8g dm$^{-3}$ of potassium hydroxide and 6.3g dm$^{-3}$ of nitric acid react together?

14. In a titration of aqueous calcium chloride with aqueous silver nitrate, 25 cm$^3$ of calcium chloride solution of concentration 0.1 mol cm$^{-3}$ is found to require 40 cm$^3$ of silver nitrate solution for complete reaction.
Calculate the concentration of the silver nitrate solution in
(a) mol dm$^{-3}$, and (b) g dm$^{-3}$.
During the reaction a precipitate is formed. What is this precipitate and what mass of it is obtained?

32

15. 20g of a compound of a halogen (X) with calcium is dissolved in 1 $dm^3$ of aqueous solution. 25 $cm^3$ of the solution reacts exactly with 20 $cm^3$ of a 0.25M aqueous solution of silver nitrate.
    Calculate the relative atomic mass of the halogen.
    Which halogen is present in the compound?

16. 0.6g of a metal $M$ from Group II of the Periodic Table was added to 50 $cm^3$ of aqueous sulphuric acid of concentration 1 mol $dm^{-3}$.
    When the reaction was complete the excess sulphuric acid required for neutralisation 100 $cm^3$ of aqueous sodium hydroxide of concentration 0.5 mol $dm^{-3}$.
    Calculate the number of moles of excess sulphuric acid and hence the number of moles of acid which reacted with the metal. Hence find the relative atomic mass of the metal.

17. A metal $X$ is in Group II of the Periodic Table and its relative atomic mass is 88.
    Write the fomula of the carbonate of $X$ and find its molar mass.
    Calculate the volume of 0.2M aqueous hydrochloric acid needed to react exactly with 0.37g of the carbonate of $X$.

18. Sodium reacts with water according to the equation

$$2Na_{(s)} + 2H_2O_{(l)} \longrightarrow 2NaOH_{(aq)} + H_{2(g)}$$

1.0g of sodium amalgam (sodium dissolved in mercury) was added to water. When all the sodium had reacted the solution formed was found to require 20 $cm^3$ of aqueous hydrochloric acid of concentration 0.5 mol $dm^{-3}$ for neutralisation.

(a) Find the number of moles of sodium hydroxide formed in the reaction and so calculate the percentage by mass of sodium in the sodium amalgam.

(b) If 1 mole of hydrogen occupies 24 $dm^3$ under the conditions of the experiment calculate the volume of hydrogen which would be given off during the above reaction of the sodium with water.

19. 20 $cm^3$ of an aqueous solution of sodium carbonate reacts with exactly 25 $cm^3$ of aqueous nitric acid of concentration 1 mol $dm^{-3}$.
    Calculate the concentration of the sodium carbonate solution, expressing your answer in
    (a) g $dm^{-3}$ of $Na_2CO_3$, and

33

(b)  g dm$^{-3}$ of $Na_2CO_3 \cdot 10H_2O$.

(c)  How many moles of sodium ions would be present in 250 cm$^3$ of the sodium carbonate solution?

20.  40 cm$^3$ of an aqueous solution of sodium hydroxide was found to neutralise 25 cm$^3$ of aqueous hydrochloric acid. When the solution left was carefully evaporated 2.34g of sodium chloride was obtained.

(a)  Find the number of moles of sodium chloride formed and hence

(b)  calculate the molarities of the sodium hydroxide and hydrochloric acid solutions.

21.  An element $X$ has a relative atomic mass of 137 and forms a hydroxide $X(OH)_2$. 20 cm$^3$ of an aqueous solution containing 85.5g dm$^{-3}$ of this hydroxide required 25 cm$^3$ of 0.8M hydrochloric acid for neutralisation. When the solution formed was evaporated 2.08g of solid was obtained.

(a)  Write the formula of this solid,

(b)  the equation for the reaction which has taken place, and

(c)  show that the above experimental results when expressed as moles of reagents are in agreement with your equation.

22.  A crystalline dibasic organic acid contains 32.0% carbon, 4.0% hydrogen and 64.0% oxygen. Find the empirical formula of the acid.

7.5g of the acid was weighed out, dissolved in water and the solution made up to 100 cm$^3$. 25 cm$^3$ of this solution required 20 cm$^3$ of aqueous sodium hydroxide of concentration 1.25 mol dm$^{-3}$ for complete neutralisation. Calculate:

(a)  the molar mass of the acid and hence

(b)  the molecular formula of the acid.

# Section E
# The gas laws and Gay-Lussac's law of combining volumes

In calculations on the gas laws the temperature must be expressed in Kelvin units (K) where

$$K = °C + 273$$

e.g. $20°C = 20 + 273 = 293K$
$-15°C = -15 + 273 = 258K$

---

**Example 1:**   A given mass of gas occupies $400 \text{ cm}^3$ at $13°C$ and a pressure of 836 mm of mercury. What volume will it occupy at s.t.p. ($0°C$ and 760 mm pressure)?

$$\frac{P_1V_1}{T_1} = \frac{P_2V_2}{T_2}$$

$P_1 = 836 \text{ mm}$ $\qquad\qquad$ $P_2 = 760 \text{ mm}$
$V_1 = 400 \text{ cm}^3$ $\qquad\qquad$ $V_2$   To be found
$T_1 = 13°C = 13 + 273 = 286K$ $\quad$ $T_2 = 0°C = 273K$

$$\frac{836 \times 400}{286} = \frac{760 \times V_2}{273}$$

$$286 \times 760 \times V_2 = 836 \times 400 \times 273$$

$$V_2 = \frac{836 \times 400 \times 273}{286 \times 760} = \underline{420 \text{ cm}^3}$$

*Questions*

1.1. Calculate the final volumes of the gases whose initial volumes are given, when the stated changes in temperature and pressure occur:

| Initial Volume | Initial Conditions | Final Conditions |
|---|---|---|
| (a)  $330 \text{ cm}^3$ | $24°C$ & $810 \text{ mm}$ | $17°C$ & $870 \text{ mm}$ |
| (b)  $560 \text{ cm}^3$ | $2°C$ & $770 \text{ mm}$ | $-23°C$ & $784 \text{ mm}$ |
| (c)  $720 \text{ cm}^3$ | $7°C$ & $840 \text{ mm}$ | $27°C$ & $800 \text{ mm}$ |
| (d)  $380 \text{ cm}^3$ | $77°C$ & $790 \text{ mm}$ | $7°C$ & $760 \text{ mm}$ |
| (e)  $390 \text{ cm}^3$ | s.t.p. | $14°C$ & $779 \text{ mm}$ |

| (f) | 1520 cm$^3$ | $-13°C$ & 780 mm | s.t.p. |
| (g) | 800 cm$^3$ | 21°C & 798 mm | s.t.p. |
| (h) | 819 cm$^3$ | s.t.p. | 26°C & 741 mm |

1.2. A given mass of gas occupies 420 cm$^3$ at 21°C and 840 mm pressure. The temperature is raised to 47°C. At what pressure (mm of mercury) will the gas occupy 480 cm$^3$ at this new temperature?

1.3. A certain mass of gas occupies 910 cm$^3$ at 13°C and 770 mm pressure. The gas is cooled until the volume is 840 cm$^3$ and its pressure is 700 mm. What is the temperature of the gas under these new conditions?

---

**Example 2:** What volume of oxygen will be required to burn 20 cm$^3$ of carbon monoxide completely and what volume of carbon dioxide will then be formed (all volumes being measured at the same temperature and pressure)?

The equation for the reaction is

$$2CO_{(g)} + O_{2(g)} \longrightarrow 2CO_{2(g)}$$

2 volumes + 1 volume $\longrightarrow$ 2 volumes

20 cm$^3$ + 10 cm$^3$ $\longrightarrow$ 20 cm$^3$

i.e. 10 cm$^3$ of oxygen are required

and 20 cm$^3$ of carbon dioxide are formed.

*Questions*

2.1. Write the relevant equations and calculate the volume of hydrogen which will react with
   (a) 50 cm$^3$ of chlorine,
   (b) 100 cm$^3$ of oxygen,
   (c) 25 cm$^3$ of nitrogen.

2.2. The equation for the complete combustion of methane is:

$$CH_{4(g)} + 2O_{2(g)} \longrightarrow CO_{2(g)} + 2H_2O_{(l)}$$

Calculate
   (a) the volume of oxygen needed for the complete combustion of 100 cm$^3$ of methane,
   (b) the volume of air needed for the complete combustion of 50 cm$^3$ of methane, assuming that air contains 20% by volume of oxygen,

(c) the volume of carbon dioxide formed when 500 cm$^3$ of methane is burned.

All volumes are measured under the same conditions.

---

**Example 3:** Calculate the volume of oxygen needed to burn 40 cm$^3$ of propane ($C_3H_8$) completely and the volumes of the products if all the volumes are measured at the same pressure and (a) at 20°C, and (b) at 105°C.

(a) At 20°C the water formed will be in the liquid state and will have a negligible volume.

$$C_3H_{8(g)} + 5O_{2(g)} \longrightarrow 3CO_{2(g)} + 4H_2O_{(l)}$$

1 volume + 5 volumes $\longrightarrow$ 3 volumes

∴ 40 cm$^3$ + 200 cm$^3$ $\longrightarrow$ 120 cm$^3$

i.e. 200 cm$^3$ of oxygen are needed

and 120 cm$^3$ of carbon dioxide are formed.

(b) At 105°C steam will be formed and its volume may be calculated.

$$C_3H_{8(g)} + 5O_{2(g)} \longrightarrow 3CO_{2(g)} + 4H_2O_{(g)}$$

1 volume + 5 volumes $\longrightarrow$ 3 volumes + 4 volumes

∴ 40 cm$^3$ + 200 cm$^3$ $\longrightarrow$ 120 cm$^3$ + 160 cm$^3$

i.e. 200 cm$^3$ of oxygen are needed,

120 cm$^3$ of carbon dioxide are formed,

and 160 cm$^3$ of steam are formed.

*Questions*

3.1. Write the equation for the reaction of hydrogen with oxygen. If 100 cm$^3$ of hydrogen and 100 cm$^3$ of oxygen are exploded together, calculate
   (a) the volume of oxygen used in reacting with the 100 cm$^3$ of hydrogen,
   (b) the volume of unused oxygen,
   (c) the total volume of gases left if all volumes are measured at room temperature,
   (d) the total volume of gases left if all volumes are measured at 105°C.

3.2. The reaction between ethene and oxygen is represented by the equation:

$$C_2H_{4(g)} + 3O_{2(g)} \longrightarrow 2CO_{2(g)} + 2H_2O_{(l)}$$

37

Calculate the volume of oxygen needed to burn 200 cm³ of ethene and the composition of the gases left if all volumes are measured (a) at room temperature, (b) just above 100°C. If air contains 20% by volume of oxygen and 80% by volume of nitrogen, calculate the volume of air needed for the complete combustion of 10 dm³ of ethene and the composition of the gases left, all volumes being measured at room temperature and pressure.

---

**Example 4:**   If all volumes are measured at room temperature and pressure, calculate the volumes of gases left when the following mixtures are exploded together:
(a)  50 cm³ of methane and 100 cm³ of oxygen,
(b)  20 cm³ of methane and 50 cm³ of oxygen,
(c)  40 cm³ of methane and 60 cm³ of oxygen.

(a)        $CH_{4(g)} + 2O_{2(g)} \longrightarrow CO_{2(g)} + 2H_2O_{(l)}$
      1 volume + 2 volumes  $\longrightarrow$  1 volume
      ∴ 50 cm³ + 100 cm³  $\longrightarrow$  100 cm³
∴ All the methane and oxygen are used up and 100 cm³ of carbon dioxide are left.
(b)  The oxygen is present in excess.
           $CH_{4(g)} + 2O_{2(g)} \longrightarrow CO_{2(g)} + 2H_2O_{(l)}$
      1 volume + 2 volumes  $\longrightarrow$  1 volume
      ∴ 20 cm³ + 40 cm³  $\longrightarrow$  20 cm³
∴ 10 cm³ of unused oxygen is left with 20 cm³ of carbon dioxide.
(c)  The methane is present in excess.
           $CH_{4(g)} + 2O_{2(g)} \longrightarrow CO_{2(g)} + 2H_2O_{(l)}$
      1 volume + 2 volumes  $\longrightarrow$  1 volume
      ∴ 30 cm³ + 60 cm³  $\longrightarrow$  30 cm³
∴ 10 cm³ of unused methane is left with 30 cm³ of carbon dioxide.

4.1.  In each of the following examples write the equation for the reaction which occurs and calculate the volumes of gases left after the reaction (all volumes are measured at room temperature and pressure).
    (a)  150 cm³ of carbon monoxide and 75 cm³ of oxygen are exploded together,

(b) 50 cm³ of carbon monoxide and 50 cm³ of oxygen are exploded together,

(c) 60 cm³ of hydrogen and 80 cm³ of chlorine are reacted together,

(d) 100 cm³ of hydrogen and 40 cm³ of oxygen are exploded together,

(e) 45 cm³ of nitrogen and 90 cm³ of hydrogen are reacted together.

4.2. The reaction between butane and oxygen is represented by the equation:

$$2C_4H_{10(g)} + 13O_{2(g)} \longrightarrow 8CO_{2(g)} + 10H_2O_{(l)}$$

If all volumes are measured at 20°C and atmospheric pressure, calculate

(a) the volume of oxygen needed to burn 1 dm³ of butane,

(b) the volume of carbon dioxide formed when 500 cm³ of butane is burned,

(c) the volumes of gases left after 40 cm³ of butane and 300 cm³ of oxygen have been reacted together,

(d) the volumes of gases left after 100 cm³ of butane and 390 cm³ of oxygen have been reacted together.

What volumes of gases would be left after the reaction in (d) if all volumes were measured at 105°C and atmospheric pressure?

*General questions*

5. What is the value of $M_r(SO_2)$?
   If 1 mole of sulphur dioxide occupies 22.4 dm³ at s.t.p. what volume will be occupied by 8g of sulphur dioxide at (a) s.t.p., and (b) 26°C and 874 mm pressure?

6. Write separate equations for the combustion of carbon monoxide and of hydrogen.
   Water gas consists of equal volumes of carbon monoxide and hydrogen.
   Calculate the volume of oxygen needed for the complete combustion of 5 dm³ of water gas.

7. Write the equation for the complete combustion of octane ($C_8H_{18}$) in oxygen.
   (a) 10 cm³ of octane vapour is exploded with 135 cm³ of oxygen. Find the ratio of the total volumes of gases left when all volumes are measured at (i) 20°C, and (ii) 105°C.
   (b) What volume of air (20% oxygen and 80% nitrogen) is

39

needed to burn 2 dm$^3$ of octane vapour completely and what will be the composition of the gases left? (All volumes are measured at room temperature and pressure)

8. Calculate the volume of oxygen required for the complete combustion of 100 cm$^3$ of a mixture of equal parts of ethene ($C_2H_4$) and ethane ($C_2H_6$) and find the volume of carbon dioxide produced, all volumes being measured at the same atmospheric temperature and pressure.
(Write separate equations for the combustion of each compound.)

9. The two gases hydrogen sulphide and sulphur dioxide react according to the equation:
$$2H_2S_{(g)} + SO_{2(g)} \longrightarrow 3S_{(s)} + 2H_2O_{(l)}$$
If all volumes are measured at room temperature and atmospheric pressure, calculate the volumes of gases left when
(a) 200 cm$^3$ of hydrogen sulphide and 100 cm$^3$ of sulphur dioxide react together,
(b) 100 cm$^3$ of hydrogen sulphide and 100 cm$^3$ of sulphur dioxide react together,
(c) 300 cm$^3$ of hydrogen sulphide and 100 cm$^3$ of sulphur dioxide react together.
(d) What volumes of gases will be left when 50 cm$^3$ of hydrogen sulphide and 50 cm$^3$ of sulphur dioxide have reacted together if all volumes are measured at 105°C?

10. Write the equation for the oxidation of ammonia to nitrogen by copper (II) oxide.
50 cm$^3$ of a mixture of ammonia and nitrogen was passed over heated copper (II) oxide. The volume of gas collected after the reaction (at the original room temperature) was 30 cm$^3$. What was the percentage of ammonia in the mixture?

11. 50 cm$^3$ of carbon monoxide was mixed with excess oxygen at 12°C and 760 mm pressure and then exploded. The residual gas occupied 88 cm$^3$ measured at 57°C and 750 mm pressure. Calculate the volume that this residual gas would occupy at 12°C and 760 mm and hence find the volume in it of unused oxygen under these conditions.

12. 50 cm$^3$ of a hydrocarbon $C_xH_y$ was mixed with 500 cm$^3$ of oxygen and the mixture was exploded. The resulting gases were cooled to the original room temperature when the volume was found to be 400 cm$^3$. After adding a strong aqueous solution of potassium hydroxide the volume

decreased to 200 cm³ and the residual gas was found to be oxygen.

Find

(a) the volume of oxygen used in the reaction,
(b) the volume of carbon dioxide formed in the reaction,
(c) the formula of the hydrocarbon.

Write the equation for the reaction of this hydrocarbon with oxygen.

# Section F
# The molar volume

(s.t.p. = 0°C or 273K and 760 mm pressure)

---

**Example 1:** 0.25g of sulphur dioxide is found to occupy 87.5 cm$^3$ at s.t.p. What volume will be occupied by one mole of sulphur dioxide at s.t.p?

$M(SO_2) = 64g$

0.25g of sulphur dioxide occupies 87.5 cm$^3$ at s.t.p.

∴ 1g of sulphur dioxide will occupy 350 cm$^3$ at s.t.p.

∴ 64g of sulphur dioxide will occupy $64 \times 350 = 22\ 400$ cm$^3$ or 22.4 dm$^3$.

This volume occupied by 1 mole of a gas is known as the <u>molar volume</u>.

The molar volume of all gases is equal to 22.4 dm$^3$ at s.t.p.

The value for the molar volume will of course vary with temperature and pressure.

*Question 1*

The following experimental results were obtained at various room temperatures and pressures. In each case find the volume occupied by 1 mole of the gas under the conditions of the experiment.

(a)  0.5g of carbon dioxide occupies 275 cm$^3$.

(b)  305 cm$^3$ of methane ($CH_4$) has a mass of 0.2g.

(c)  1.25g of butane ($C_4H_{10}$) occupies 500 cm$^3$.

(d)  0.8g of oxygen occupies 595 cm$^3$.

(e)  305 cm$^3$ of nitrogen has a mass of 0.35g.

What is the average value of all your results?

---

**Example 2:** 1 mole of a gas occupies 22.4 dm$^3$ at s.t.p.

$\frac{1}{2}$ mole of a gas occupies 11.2 dm$^3$ at s.t.p.

0.1 mole of a gas occupies 2.24 dm$^3$ at s.t.p.

$\frac{1}{40}$ mole of a gas occupies $(\frac{1}{40}) \times 22.4 = 0.56$ dm$^3$ or 560 cm$^3$ at s.t.p., etc.

22.4 dm$^3$ (or 22 400 cm$^3$) at s.t.p. represents 1 mole of a gas.
5.6 dm$^3$ at s.t.p. represents $\frac{1}{4}$ mole of a gas.
112 cm$^3$ at s.t.p. represents $112/22\ 400 = 1/200$ mole, etc.

*Questions*
2.1. Find the volume occupied by the following quantities at s.t.p.:
    (a) 1 mole of oxygen,
    (b) $\frac{1}{5}$ mole of nitrogen,
    (c) $1\frac{1}{2}$ moles of carbon dioxide,
    (d) 0.15 mole of carbon monoxide,
    (e) $\frac{1}{50}$ mole of methane,
    (f) $x$ mole of ammonia.
2.2. Assuming that 1 mole of a gas occupies 24 dm$^3$ (24 000 cm$^3$) at room temperature and pressure, find the volume occupied by the following quantities under these conditions:
    (a) $\frac{1}{4}$ mole of carbon dioxide,
    (b) 3.2 moles of nitrogen,
    (c) 0.02 mole of hydrogen,
    (d) 1.35 moles of oxygen,
    (e) 0.125 mole of carbon monoxide.
2.3. How many moles are represented by the following volumes measured at s.t.p?
    (a) 22.4 dm$^3$ of ammonia,
    (b) 2.24 dm$^3$ of hydrogen,
    (c) 56 dm$^3$ of oxygen,
    (d) 672 cm$^3$ of carbon dioxide,
    (e) $x$ cm$^3$ of butane.
2.4. Assuming that 1 mole of a gas occupies 24 dm$^3$ at room temperature and pressure, find the number of moles represented by the following volumes measured under these conditions:
    (a) 2 dm$^3$ of hydrogen sulphide,
    (b) 0.6 dm$^3$ of nitrogen,
    (c) 1 600 cm$^3$ of methane,
    (d) 12 cm$^3$ of oxygen,
    (e) 288 cm$^3$ of carbon dioxide.

---

**Example 3:** If the molar volume of a gas at room temperature and pressure is 24 dm$^3$, what volume is occupied by 5.5 g of carbon dioxide under these conditions?

$M(CO_2) = 12 + 32 = 44g$

$\therefore$ 5.5g of carbon dioxide = $5.5/44 = \frac{1}{8}$ mole

1 mole of carbon dioxide occupies 24 dm$^3$

$\therefore \frac{1}{8}$ mole of carbon dioxide occupies 3 dm$^3$.

## Question 3

If 1 mole of a gas occupies 24 dm$^3$ (24 000 cm$^3$) at room temperature and pressure, find the volume occupied by the following masses under these conditions:

(a) 16g of sulphur dioxide,

(b) 40g of methane ($CH_4$),

(c) 1g of oxygen,

(d) 0.51g of ammonia,

(e) 100g of helium.

---

**Example 4:** If 1 mole of a gas occupies 22 400 cm$^3$ at s.t.p., what is the mass of 560 cm$^3$ of hydrogen sulphide at s.t.p?

22 400 cm$^3$ of hydrogen sulphide represents 1 mole

$\therefore$ 560 cm$^3$ of hydrogen sulphide represents 560/22 400 = $\frac{1}{40}$ mole

$M(H_2S) = 2 + 32 = 34g$

$\therefore$ 1 mole of hydrogen sulphide = 34g

$\therefore \frac{1}{40}$ mole of hydrogen sulphide = $\frac{34}{40} = \underline{0.85g}$

## Question 4

Assuming that the molar volume of a gas is 24 dm$^3$ (24 000 cm$^3$) at room temperature and pressure, calculate the masses of the following volumes of gases under these conditions:

(a) 12 dm$^3$ of butane ($C_4H_{10}$),

(b) 1 dm$^3$ of oxygen,

(c) 60 cm$^3$ of sulphur dioxide,

(d) 100 dm$^3$ of propene ($C_3H_6$),

(e) 3 cm$^3$ of bromine vapour.

---

**Example 5:** 50 cm$^3$ of a gas at s.t.p. is found to have a mass of 0.125g. What is the relative molecular mass of the gas?

(Molar volume = 22 400 cm$^3$ at s.t.p.)

50 cm$^3$ of the gas at s.t.p. weigh 0.125g

$\therefore$ 100 cm$^3$ of the gas at s.t.p. weigh 0.25g

44

∴ 1 000 cm$^3$ of the gas at s.t.p. weigh 2.5g
∴ 22 400 cm$^3$ of the gas at s.t.p. weigh 2.5 × 22.4 = 56g
i.e. 56g of the gas must be 1 mole.
The relative molecular mass = 56

## Question 5
Find the relative molecular masses of the following gases:
(a) 4.5 dm$^3$ of gas A at room temperature and pressure have a
    mass of 3.0g;
(b) 800 cm$^3$ of gas B at s.t.p. have a mass of 1.5g;
(c) 0.2g of gas C occupies 70 cm$^3$ at s.t.p.;
(d) 100g of gas D are found to occupy 600 dm$^3$ measured at room
    temperature and pressure.
(Assume that the molar volume at room temperature and pressure
is 24 dm$^3$.)

---

**Example 6:**   Calculate the volume of ammonia, measured at
atmospheric temperature and pressure, which may be obtained by
reacting 3.3g of ammonium sulphate with excess calcium
hydroxide.
(Molar volume under the conditions of the experiment = 24 dm$^3$.)
The equation for the reaction is:
$(NH_4)_2SO_{4(s)} + Ca(OH)_{2(s)} \longrightarrow 2NH_{3(g)} + CaSO_{4(s)} + 2H_2O_{(l)}$
(a) The molar mass of ammonium sulphate,
    $M[(NH_4)_2SO_4]$ = 28 + 8 + 32 + 64 = 132
∴ 3.3g of ammonium sulphate = 3.3/132 = $\frac{1}{40}$ mole
(b) From the equation,
1 mole of ammonium sulphate will give 2 moles of ammonia.
∴ $\frac{1}{40}$ mole of ammonium sulphate will give $\frac{1}{20}$ mole of ammonia.
(c) 1 mole of ammonia will occupy 24 dm$^3$
∴ $\frac{1}{20}$ mole of ammonia will occupy $\frac{24}{20}$ = 1.2 dm$^3$
i.e. 1.2 dm$^3$ of ammonia may be obtained.

## Question 6
In the following examples, calculate
 (i) the number of moles of the given reagent which are used,
 (ii) the number of moles of gas which are formed in the reaction,
 (iii) the volume which this quantity of gas will occupy at atmos-
      pheric temperature and pressure. (Assume that the molar
      volume under these conditions is 24 dm$^3$ or 24 000 cm$^3$)
(a) 15g of calcium carbonate are reacted with dilute hydrochloric

acid solution to form carbon dioxide according to the equation:
$$CaCO_{3(s)} + 2HCl_{(aq)} \longrightarrow CaCl_{2(aq)} + CO_{2(g)} + H_2O_{(l)}$$

(b) 0.8g of calcium carbide ($CaC_2$) is added to water to form ethyne ($C_2H_2$):
$$CaC_{2(s)} + 2H_2O_{(l)} \longrightarrow Ca(OH)_{2(s)} + C_2H_{2(g)}$$

(c) Concentrated sulphuric acid containing 1.4g of the acid is heated with excess copper to form sulphur dioxide:
$$Cu_{(s)} + 2H_2SO_{4(aq)} \longrightarrow$$
$$CuSO_{4(aq)} + SO_{2(g)} + 2H_2O_{(l)}$$

(d) 0.79g of potassium permanganate is added to concentrated hydrochloric acid to form chlorine:
$$2KMnO_{4(s)} + 16HCl_{(aq)} \longrightarrow$$
$$2KCl_{(aq)} + 2MnCl_{2(aq)} + 5Cl_{2(g)} + 8H_2O_{(l)}$$

---

**Example 7:** Carbon dioxide was passed slowly over strongly heated carbon until 96 cm³ of carbon monoxide (measured at atmospheric temperature and pressure) had been collected. Calculate the mass of carbon which had reacted.
(Molar volume under the given conditions = 24 000 cm³)
The equation for the reaction is:
$$C_{(s)} + CO_{2(g)} \longrightarrow 2CO_{(g)}$$

(a) 24 000 cm³ of carbon monoxide represent 1 mole
∴ 24 cm³ of carbon monoxide represent 1/1 000 mole
∴ 96 cm³ of carbon monoxide represent 4/1 000
or 1/250 mole

(b) From the equation,
2 moles of carbon monoxide are formed from 1 mole of carbon
∴ 1/250 mole of carbon monoxide are formed from 1/500 mole of carbon

(c) Molar mass of carbon = 12g
∴ 1/500 mole of carbon = (1/500) × 12 = 0.024g
i.e. 0.024g of carbon is used in the reaction.

*Questions*
(Assume that the molar volume under the conditions in all these questions = 24 000 cm³)

7.1. Ammonia reacts with heated copper (II) oxide according to the equation:
$$2NH_{3(g)} + 3CuO_{(s)} \longrightarrow N_{2(g)} + 3Cu_{(s)} + 3H_2O_{(l)}$$

480 cm³ of ammonia measured under atmospheric conditions was passed over heated copper (II) oxide.
Calculate
(a) the number of moles of ammonia which were used,
(b) the number of moles of copper (II) oxide which were reduced,
(c) the mass of copper (II) oxide which was reduced during the experiment.

7.2. 27.4g of red lead ($Pb_3O_4$) was heated until no further reaction occurred. The oxide decomposed according to the equation:
$$2Pb_3O_{4(s)} \longrightarrow 6PbO_{(s)} + O_{2(g)}$$
Calculate:
(a) the number of moles of red lead which were used,
(b) the number of moles of oxygen which were formed,
(c) the volume at room temperature occupied by this oxygen.

7.3. When iron pyrites ($FeS_2$) is heated in oxygen the reaction is:
$$4FeS_{2(s)} + 11O_{2(g)} \longrightarrow 2Fe_2O_{3(s)} + 8SO_{2(g)}$$
If 132 dm³ of oxygen, measured at room temperature, reacted completely with iron pyrites, calculate:
(a) the number of moles of oxygen used,
(b) the number of moles of iron pyrites which reacted, and
(c) the mass of iron pyrites which reacted.
(d) What volume of sulphur dioxide (measured under the same atmospheric conditions as the volume of oxygen) would be formed in the reaction?

7.4. Steam passed over red-hot iron reacts according to the equation:
$$3Fe_{(s)} + 4H_2O_{(g)} \longrightarrow Fe_3O_{4(s)} + 4H_{2(g)}$$
In such an experiment 2 dm³ of hydrogen were collected under atmospheric conditions. Calculate:
(a) the number of moles of hydrogen formed,
(b) the number of moles of iron which had reacted,
(c) the mass of iron which had reacted.


*General questions*
(Assume that at room temperature and pressure the molar volume is 24 000 cm³)
8. Which quantity contains the greater number of molecules, 6.9g of liquid ethanol ($C_2H_6O$) or 3.36 dm³ of carbon dioxide measured at room temperature and pressure?

9. Find the ratio of the masses of equal volumes of hydrogen, helium, methane ($CH_4$) and oxygen.

10. A gas is known to be argon or carbon dioxide or propene ($C_3H_6$). 200 cm³ of the gas measured at room temperature and pressure is found to weigh 0.35g. What is the gas?

11. Calculate the volume occupied by 0.5g of carbon monoxide
    (a) at s.t.p.,
    (b) at 13°C and 770 mm pressure.

12. Assuming air to be composed of 80% nitrogen and 20% oxygen by volume, find the mass of 1 dm³ of air at room temperature and pressure.
    Find the masses of (a) 1 dm³ of methane ($CH_4$), and (b) 1 dm³ of propane ($C_3H_8$) under the same conditions.
    (c) How would you expect these two gases to be collected in the laboratory other than over water?

13. 1.74g of the gas butane ($C_4H_{10}$) was found to occupy 760 cm³ at 39°C and 768 mm pressure. What value does this information give for the molar volume of butane (a) under the conditions of the experiment, and (b) at s.t.p?

14. An organic compound is known to have the empirical formula $CH_2$. 500 cm³ of the vapour of the compound weighed 2.5g at s.t.p.
    Find the molecular formula of the compound by first finding its relative molecular mass.

15. When methane ($CH_4$) is passed over heated copper (II) oxide it is oxidised to carbon dioxide and water while the copper (II) oxide is reduced to copper.
    Write the equation for the reaction.
    If 600 cm³ of methane measured at room temperature and pressure is passed over heated copper (II) oxide what decrease in the mass of the oxide will occur?

16. Excess sodium hydrogen carbonate was added to 10 cm³ of an aqueous solution of sulphuric acid. The carbon dioxide given off in the reaction measured 72 cm³ at room temperature and pressure.
    Write the equation for the reaction and calculate the concentration of the sulphuric acid solution in moles dm⁻³.

17. 600 cm³ of carbon dioxide measured at room temperature and pressure were passed into sodium hydroxide solution so that sodium carbonate was formed.
    (a) Calculate the mass of sodium carbonate ($Na_2CO_3$) formed in the reaction.

(b) If 50% of this sodium carbonate was crystallised out as $Na_2CO_3 \cdot 10H_2O$, calculate the mass of crystals obtained.

18. When the organic compound urea ($N_2H_4CO$) is warmed with an aqueous solution of sodium hydroxide, ammonia is given off and a solution of sodium carbonate is left.

   (a) Write the equation for this reaction and calculate the volume of ammonia, measured at room temperature and pressure, which would be formed if 1 g of urea was warmed with excess sodium hydroxide solution.

   (b) If this ammonia was dissolved in water calculate the volume of a solution containing $2.5\ mol\ dm^{-3}$ of hydrochloric acid which would be required to neutralise the ammonia solution.

19. Write the equation for the reaction of sodium sulphite with dilute hydrochloric acid.

   (a) What volume of sulphur dioxide, measured at s.t.p., would be obtained by reacting 0.9g of sodium sulphite with excess aqueous hydrochloric acid solution?

   (b) What volume would the same mass of sulphur dioxide occupy if it were collected at 39°C and 768 mm pressure?

20. Chlorine was prepared by the action of concentrated hydrochloric acid on manganese (IV) oxide. The volume of gas collected was 152 cm$^3$ measured at 39°C and 800 mm pressure.
   Calculate the volume that this gas would occupy at s.t.p. and hence find the mass of hydrochloric acid (HCl) that was used in this reaction.

# Section G
# Miscellaneous questions

(Molar volume at s.t.p. = 22 400 cm³. Unless otherwise stated, assume that the molar volume at room temperature and pressure = 24 000 cm³)

1. 1.70 g of antimony sulphide is found to contain 1.22g of antimony (Sb). What is the simplest formula of the compound?
   If the molar mass of the compound is 340 what is its molecular formula?
   The compound reacts with hydrochloric acid to form hydrogen sulphide and antimony (III) chloride. Write the equation for the reaction and calculate the volume of hydrogen sulphide which could be obtained at room temperature and pressure from 1.7g of antimony sulphide.

2. 2.0g of calcium combines with 0.1g of hydrogen to form calcium hydride. What is the empirical formula of the compound?
   The calcium hydride reacts with water to form calcium hydroxide and hydrogen. Write the equation for the reaction, using the formula you have found.
   What volume of hydrogen will be obtained by the reaction of 0.21g of calcium hydride with water if the gas volume is measured at (a) s.t.p., (b) 13°C and 800 mm pressure?

3. When 2.1g of sodium hydrogen carbonate was heated until no further loss in mass occurred 300 cm³ of carbon dioxide measured at room temperature and pressure were given off and the residue was 1.325g of anhydrous sodium carbonate. Express these quantities as moles of the different substances and show that your answers agree with the equation for the reaction which occurs.
   What mass of water will also be formed in the reaction?

4. 1.8g of magnesium combines with 0.7g of nitrogen to form

magnesium nitride. Find the empirical formula of the compound.

Assuming that this is also the molecular formula, calculate the masses of the elements required to form 250g of the compound.

The magnesium nitride reacts with water to form magnesium hydroxide and ammonia. Write the balanced equation for this reaction and find the volume of ammonia given off at room temperature and pressure when 2g of the compound reacts with water.

What volume of a solution containing 1 mol dm$^{-3}$ of sulphuric acid will be neutralised by this ammonia?

5.  5.0g of a sulphide of copper is roasted in air so that all the sulphur present is converted into sulphur dioxide. The sulphur dioxide formed occupied 700 cm$^3$ at s.t.p. Find:
    (a)  the mass of sulphur dioxide formed,
    (b)  the mass of sulphur present,
    (c)  the empirical formula of the copper sulphide.

6.  Sodium peroxide ($Na_2O_2$) was added to warm water when the reaction was:
$$2Na_2O_{2(s)} + 2H_2O_{(l)} \longrightarrow 4NaOH_{(aq)} + O_{2(g)}$$
During the reaction 120 cm$^3$ of oxygen measured at room temperature and pressure was collected. Calculate
    (a)  the mass of sodium peroxide used in the reaction,
    (b)  the volume of an aqueous solution containing 0.5 mol dm$^{-3}$ of sulphuric acid needed to neutralise the solution of sodium hydroxide formed.

7.  0.6g of sodium hydride (NaH) was reacted with water when it reacted completely to form a solution of sodium hydroxide and hydrogen. The resulting sodium hydroxide solution was then made up to 250 cm$^3$.
    Write a balanced equation for the reaction and calculate
    (a)  the concentration of the final sodium hydroxide solution in g dm$^{-3}$,
    (b)  the volume of hydrogen, measured at s.t.p., formed in the reaction.

8.  In the experimental determination of the relative molecular mass of a gas, a plastic bottle was weighed when full of air and then when completely filled with a gaseous alkene. The following results were obtained:
    Mass of bottle + air = 56.30g
    Mass of bottle + alkene = 57.87g

Capacity of bottle = 1 400 cm³
Atmospheric temperature = 21°C
Atmospheric press. = 760 mm
(Density of air under the conditions of the experiment = 1.20 g dm⁻³.)

Calculate
(a) the mass of air contained in the bottle,
(b) the mass of the bottle only,
(c) the mass of the alkene,
(d) the volume of the alkene at s.t.p.,
(e) the relative molecular mass of the alkene.
What is the formula of the alkene used in the experiment?

9. The sulphide $X_2S_3$ of a metal X reacts with aqueous hydrochloric acid to form hydrogen sulphide according to the equation:

$$X_2S_{3(s)} + 6HCl_{(aq)} \longrightarrow 2XCl_{3(aq)} + 3H_2S_{(g)}$$

When 0.41 g of the sulphide was reacted with excess aqueous hydrochloric acid $101\frac{1}{3}$ cm³ of hydrogen sulphide were collected at 13°C and 880 mm pressure. Calculate
(a) the volume that the hydrogen sulphide would occupy at s.t.p.,
(b) the number of moles of hydrogen sulphide formed and hence the number of moles of the sulphide $X_2S_3$ used in the reaction,
(c) the molar mass of $X_2S_3$ and hence the relative atomic mass of X.

10. Write the equation for the reaction of magnesium with a dilute aqueous solution of hydrochloric acid.

In experiment I, 0.24 g of magnesium ribbon was added to 25 cm³ of an aqueous solution containing 1 mol dm⁻³ of hydrochloric acid at 15°C.

In experiment II, 0.24 g of magnesium ribbon was added to 25 cm³ of an aqueous solution containing 0.5 mol dm⁻³ of hydrochloric acid at 15°C.

(a) In which experiment will there be the greater initial rate of reaction?
(b) If powdered magnesium were used instead of the ribbon, what effect would this have on the rates of reaction?
(c) Will all the magnesium react in both experiments?
(d) What volume of hydrogen, measured at s.t.p., will be formed in each experiment?

In either experiment, would the volume of hydrogen formed be doubled by
- (i) warming the acid to 30°C,
- (ii) doubling the mass of magnesium but keeping the volume of acid the same,
- (iii) doubling the volume of acid used but keeping the mass of magnesium the same?

11. Write the equation for the reaction of copper (II) carbonate with aqueous hydrochloric acid.

Four separate experiments were carried out using lumps of copper (II) carbonate and an aqueous solution of hydrochloric acid of concentration 1.5 mol dm$^{-3}$.

Experiment I: 0.93g of copper (II) carbonate was added to 10 cm$^3$ of acid;

Experiment II: 0.93g of copper (II) carbonate was added to 20 cm$^3$ of acid;

Experiment III: 1.86g of copper (II) carbonate was added to 10 cm$^3$ of acid;

Experiment IV: 1.86g of copper (II) carbonate was added to 25 cm$^3$ of acid.

In each case the carbon dioxide evolved was collected under the same atmospheric conditions.

- (a) In which experiments will the volumes of carbon dioxide given off be the same?
- (b) In which experiment(s) will some copper (II) carbonate be unreacted after the reaction has finished?
- (c) In which experiment(s) will some hydrochloric acid be unreacted after the reaction has finished?

State **two** ways in which the rate of reaction in all the experiments could be increased.

12. The same quantity of electricity (i.e. the same number of electrons) was passed through three aqueous solutions containing respectively copper (II) sulphate, silver nitrate and sulphuric acid.

The cathode reactions in the solutions were:

Copper (II) sulphate solution: $Cu^{2+}_{(aq)} + 2e^- \longrightarrow Cu_{(s)}$

Silver nitrate solution: $Ag^+_{(aq)} + e^- \longrightarrow Ag_{(s)}$

Sulphuric acid solution: $2H^+_{(aq)} + 2e^- \longrightarrow H_{2(g)}$

If the mass of silver deposited from the silver nitrate solution was 0.18g, calculate

- (a) the number of moles of silver deposited,

(b)  the number of moles, and hence the mass, of copper
deposited from the copper (II) sulphate solution,
(c)  the number of moles of hydrogen liberated from the
sulphuric acid solution and hence its volume
(i)  at s.t.p., and
(ii)  at 13°C and 800 mm pressure.

13.  An organic compound has the formula $C_6H_xSO_3$. 0.79g of the
compound was oxidised vigorously so that all the sulphur was
converted into sulphuric acid. This was then reacted with
aqueous barium chloride solution when 1.165g of barium
sulphate was precipitated. Calculate
(a)  the mass of sulphur in the 1.165g of barium sulphate,
(b)  the percentage of sulphur in the organic compound.
What value does this percentage of sulphur give for x in the
formula of the organic compound?

14.  An organic compound contains carbon, hydrogen and oxygen
only and has a molar mass of 60g. 1g of the compound was
oxidised completely when 2.2g of carbon dioxide and 1.2g of
water were produced.
Calculate the masses of carbon and hydrogen present and
hence the percentage composition of the organic compound.
Find the molecular formula of the compound.

15.  An organic compound contains 40.0% of carbon, 6.66% of
hydrogen and 53.33% of oxygen. What is its empirical
formula?
0.9g of the compound is vapourised at 91°C and 760 mm
pressure and the vapour is found to occupy 448 cm³.
(a)  What volume would this mass of vapour occupy at s.t.p?
(b)  Calculate the relative molecular mass of the compound
and hence find its molecular formula.
The compound is an acid and 3g of it reacts exactly with
25 cm³ of an aqueous solution containing 80g of sodium
hydroxide per dm³.
Express this statement in terms of moles of the two substances and hence write an equation for the reaction of the
acid with sodium hydroxide.
(c)  What is the basicity of the acid?

16.  (a)  What is the percentage of nitrogen by mass in ammonium nitrate, $NH_4NO_3$?
(b)  An impure sample of ammonium nitrate is found to
contain 28% of nitrogen. What is the percentage by mass
of impurities in the sample?

54

(c) Write a balanced equation for the reaction which occurs when ammonium nitrate is warmed with an aqueous solution of sodium hydroxide.

What mass of sodium hydroxide would be required to react completely with 1g of the above impure sample of ammonium nitrate and what volume of ammonia would be formed in this reaction if the gas volume was measured

    (d) at s.t.p., and

    (e) at 39°C and 800 mm pressure?

17. (a) 0.92g of a gaseous oxide of nitrogen is found to contain 0.28g of nitrogen.

    What is the empirical formula of the compound?

    (b) 600 cm$^3$ of the oxide weighs 2.3g at room temperature and pressure.

Calculate the molar mass of the oxide and hence its molecular formula.

    (c) The oxide reacts with an aqueous sodium hydroxide solution to give a mixture of sodium nitrate, sodium nitrite and water.

Write a balanced equation for the reaction and calculate the volume of an aqueous solution containing 0.5 mole dm$^{-3}$ of sodium hydroxide which would be neutralised by 480 cm$^3$ of the gas measured at room temperature and pressure.

18. Some ores of iron are represented by the following formulae:

    (i) $Fe_2O_3$

    (ii) $Fe_3O_4$

    (iii) $FeCO_3$

    (iv) $FeS_2$

    (v) $2Fe_2O_3 \cdot 3H_2O$

    (a) Which of the above ores contains the greatest percentage by mass of iron?

    (b) If iron is obtained from the oxides $Fe_2O_3$ and $Fe_3O_4$ by reduction with carbon monoxide, which oxide requires the larger volume of carbon monoxide (measured at s.t.p.) per Kg of iron produced?

    (c) If the first stage in the extraction of iron from the ore $FeS_2$ is roasting in air when sulphur dioxide is obtained, what is the maximum volume of sulphur dioxide which can be produced per Kg of iron in the ore if the gas is measured at 546°C and 760 mm pressure?

19. A liquid compound in petrol contains carbon and hydrogen only and is found to contain 84% by mass of carbon.

(a) What is the empirical formula of the compound?
600 cm³ of the vapour of the compound at room temperature and pressure weighs 2.5g.

(b) Find the relative molecular mass of the compound and hence its molecular formula.

(c) If 25 Kg of the compound is converted into vapour at room temperature and pressure, what volume will the vapour occupy?

(d) Write the equation for the complete combustion of the petrol in oxygen to form carbon dioxide and water, and calculate the volume of oxygen measured at room temperature and pressure needed to burn the above quantity of petrol vapour.

(e) If air consists of 20% oxygen and 80% nitrogen, find the volume of air needed to burn this volume of petrol vapour and the total volume of gases left after the combustion (all volumes being measured at room temperature and pressure).

20. (a) The chloride of a metal X reacts with moderately concentrated sulphuric acid according to the equation:

$$XCl_{2(s)} + H_2SO_{4(aq)} \longrightarrow 2HCl_{(g)} + XSO_{4(aq)}$$

2.22g of $XCl_2$ was warmed with sulphuric acid until no further reaction occurred, the hydrogen chloride evolved was dissolved in water and the solution then made up to 500 cm³. 25 cm³ of this aqueous hydrochloric acid solution was found to require for neutralisation 20 cm³ of an aqueous solution containing 5.6g dm⁻³ of potassium hydroxide. Calculate the number of moles of hydrogen chloride which were formed in the reaction, the molar mass of $XCl_2$ and hence the relative atomic mass of X.

(b) 0.37g of this same chloride $XCl_2$ is found to combine with 320 cm³ of gaseous ammonia measured at room temperature and pressure to form a compound $XCl_2 \cdot yNH_3$. Calculate the number of moles of $XCl_2$ and ammonia involved and so find the value of y.

# Answers

---

**Section A**
**1.1**   (a)  H = 2, O = 1
      (b)  Cu = 1, S = 1, O = 4
      (c)  N = 2, H = 8, S = 1, O = 4
      (d)  Al = 1, N = 3, O = 9
      (e)  K = 4, Fe = 1, C = 6, N = 6
      (f)  N = 2, H = 8, Cr = 2, O = 7
      (g)  Fe = 2, S = 3, O = 12
      (h)  Mg = 1, S = 1, O = 11, H = 14
      (i)  Na = 2, C = 1, O = 13, H = 20
**1.2.**  (a)  80
      (b)  44
      (c)  98
      (d)  138
      (e)  68
      (f)  310
      (g)  342
      (h)  287
      (i)  331
      (j)  392
**2.1.**  (a)  24g
      (b)  12g
      (c)  2.4g
      (d)  48g
      (e)  80g
      (f)  6g
      (g)  .96g
      (h)  24xg
**2.2**  Mass = No. of moles $\times$ $A_r$
**2.3**  (a)  1 mole
      (b)  0.25 mole
      (c)  0.6 mole
      (d)  1.5 moles
      (e)  0.05 mole
      (f)  0.003 mole
      (g)  4.25 moles
      (h)  x/40 mole
**2.4.**  No. of moles = Mass/$A_r$

**2.5.** (a) 9g
(b) 14.4g
(c) 130g
(d) 16g
(e) 8.28g
(f) 130g
(g) 0.325g
(h) 0.345g

**2.6.** (a) 0.75 mole
(b) 0.2 mole
(c) $\frac{1}{9}$ (0.111) mole
(d) 3.125 mole
(e) $\frac{3}{7}$ (0.429) mole
(f) 0.01 mole
(g) $\frac{1}{90}$ (0.011) mole
(h) 0.0025 mole

**3.1.** (a) 1 mole
(b) 0.5 mole
(c) 0.125 mole
(d) 2.5 mole
(e) 0.05 mole
(f) 0.01 mole
(g) 0.0025 mole
(h) $x/120$ mole

**3.2.** (a) 160g
(b) 40g
(c) 16g
(d) 500g
(e) 4g
(f) 0.8g
(g) 200g
(h) 160xg

**3.3.** (a) 0.15 mole
(b) $\frac{1}{12}$ (0.0833) mole
(c) 0.25 mole
(d) 0.1 mole
(e) 1.25 moles
(f) 0.005 mole
(g) 0.05 mole
(h) 2.5 moles
(i) 0.02 mole
(j) 0.125 mole

**3.4.** (a) 80.5g
(b) 30g
(c) 282g
(d) 12.6g
(e) 6.62g
(f) 384g
(g) 168g
(h) 7.15g

(i) 1.23g

**4.1.** (a) 4g
(b) 53.33g
(c) 160g
(d) 1.6g
(e) 76.8g
(f) 0.16g

**4.2.** (a) 3g
(b) 30g
(c) 21g
(d) 30g

**5.1.** (a) 0.15 mole $Ca^{2+}$
0.15 mole $CO_3^{2-}$
(b) 5 moles $NH_4^+$
2.5 moles $SO_4^{2-}$
(c) 0.5 mole $Ca^{2+}$
0.33 mole $PO_4^{3-}$

**5.2.** (a) 0.25 mole AgBr,
0.25 mole $Ag^+$,
0.25 mole $Br^-$
(b) 0.025 mole $BaCl_2$,
0.025 mole $Ba^{2+}$
0.05 mole $Cl^-$
(c) 0.015 mole $Al_2(SO_4)_3$
0.03 mole $Al^{3+}$
0.045 mole $SO_4^{2-}$

**6.** (a) 1.6 moles
(b) 21.6 moles
(c) 0.75 mole

**7.** (a) 25 cm$^3$
(b) 20 cm$^3$
(c) 480 cm$^3$

**8.** (a) 14g of iron
(b) 4g of silicon
(c) 26g of zinc
(d) 4g of magnesium
(e) 3g of aluminium
(f) 54g of magnesium
(g) 182g of iron
(h) $\frac{1}{6}$g of calcium

**9.** 2g $Br_2$, 0.2g $CH_4$, 0.4g $O_2$

**10.** 13.25g of sodium carbonate

**11.** 8g of iron (III) sulphate

**12.** 8g of sulphur dioxide

**13.** (a) 30.8g
(b) 63.8g
a

**14.** c > b > f > d
e

**Section B**
1.   (a) $CaCl_2$
    (b) $K_2S$
    (c) $Ag_2O$
    (d) $PbO_2$
    (e) $PCl_5$
    (f) $Mg_3N_2$
    (g) $ZnBr_2$
    (h) $N_2O_5$
    (i) $Fe_3O_4$
    (j) $Mn_2O_7$

2.1. (a) $SO_2$
    (b) $CaH_2$
    (c) $FeBr_3$
    (d) $MnO_2$
    (e) $Al_2O_3$
    (f) $CaCl_2$

2.2. (a) $ZnO$
    (b) $FeS_2$
    (c) $Cr_2O_3$
    (d) $NO_2$
    (e) $P_2O_3$
    (f) $AsH_3$
    (g) $CaC_2$
    (h) $I_2O_5$
    (i) $SiF_4$
    (j) $Na_3P$

3.   (a) $K_2S$
    (b) $AlCl_3$
    (c) $Pb_3O_4$

4.   (a) (i) $AlCl_3$
       (ii) $Al_2Cl_6$
    (b) (i) $CH_2$
       (ii) $C_4H_8$
    (c) (i) $P_2O_5$
       (ii) $P_4O_{10}$

5.   (a) $CH_2O$
    (b) $C_3H_9N$
    (c) $K_4FeC_6N_6$
    (d) $Na_2S_2O_3$

6.   (a) (i) 3.6g water
       (ii) $M_r(CuSO_4) = 160$
       (iii) $CuSO_4 \cdot 5H_2O$
    (b) (i) 2.10g water
       (ii) $M_r(MgSO_4) = 120$
       (iii) $MgSO_4 \cdot 7H_2O$
    (c) (i) 3.6g water
       (ii) $M_r(CaCl_2) = 111$
       (iii) $CaCl_2 \cdot 6H_2O$
    (d) (i) 3.6g $H_2C_2O_4$

        (ii)  $M_r(H_2C_2O_4) = 90$
        (iii)  $H_2C_2O_4 \cdot 2H_2O$
7.    (a)  60%
      (b)  24.7%
      (c)  29%
      (d)  35%
      (e)  36%
8.    $x = 7$
9.    $C_4H_8O_2$
10.   (a)  26.5%
      (b)  $\frac{1}{5}$
11.   $A$:$CrO_3$
      $B$:$Cr_2O_3$
      $4CrO_{3(s)} \longrightarrow 2Cr_2O_{3(s)} + 3O_{2(g)}$
12.   $Fe_3O_4$
      $Fe_3O_{4(s)} + 4H_{2(g)} \longrightarrow 3Fe_{(s)} + 4H_2O_{(l)}$
13.   5.6g carbon monoxide
      $x = 4$
14.   $HgCl_2$
      $HgCl$
      $Hg_2Cl_2$
15.   $x = 10$
      $M(Na_2CO_3 \cdot 10H_2O) = 286g$
      $y = 1$
16.   $MnO_2$
      $Al_2O_3$
      $3MnO_{2(s)} + 4Al_{(s)} \longrightarrow 3Mn_{(s)} + 2Al_2O_{3(s)}$
17.   $Y$:$C_7H_{16}$
      $Z$:$C_3H_6$
      $X$:$C_{13}H_{28}$

---

**Section C**
1.1.   (a)  0.125 mole
       (b)  0.125 mole
       (c)  8g
1.2.   (a)  0.2 mole
       (b)  0.2 mole
       (c)  11.7g
1.3.   (a)  0.05 mole
       (b)  0.05 mole
       (c)  6.2g
1.4    (a)  0.02 mole
       (b)  0.02 mole
       (c)  0.88g
1.5    (a)  0.0833 mole
       (b)  0.0833 mole
       (c)  19.42g
2.1.   (a)  0.1 mole
       (b)  0.05 mole

60

(c) 1.4g
**2.2.** (a) 0.025 mole
  (b) 0.025 mole
  (c) 1.1g
  (d) 0.6 dm$^3$
**2.3.** (a) 0.125 mole
  (b) 0.0625 mole
  (c) 10g
**2.4.** (a) 0.04 mole
  (b) 0.08 mole
  (c) 3.2g
**2.5.** (a) 0.03 mole
  (b) 0.01 mole iron (III) sulphate
    0.03 mole barium chloride
  (c) 4g iron (III) sulphate
    6.24g barium chloride
**2.6.** (a) 2.5 moles
  (b) 0.833 mole
  (c) 120g
**3.1.** (a) 0.01 mole
  (b) M(ZO) = 80g
    $A_r$(Z) = 64
**3.2.** (a) 0.02 mole
  (b) 0.02 mole
  (c) M(R$_2$SO$_4$) = 174g
    $A_r$(R) = 39
**3.3** (a) 0.15 mole
  (b) 0.05 mole
  (c) M(Q$_2$O$_3$) = 102g
    $A_r$(Q) = 27
**3.4.** (a) 0.06 mole
  (b) 0.01 mole
  (c) M(X$_2$O$_3$) = 160g
    $A_r$(X) = 56
**4.** (a) M(MgO) = 40g
  (b) M(H$_2$SO$_4$) = 98g
  (c) M(MgSO$_4$) = 120g

| Mass of MgO used | No. of moles of MgO used | No. of moles of H$_2$SO$_4$ used | Mass of H$_2$SO$_4$ used | No. of moles of MgSO$_4$ formed | Mass of MgSO$_4$ formed |
|---|---|---|---|---|---|
| | 0.5 | 0.5 | 49g | | |
| 1.0g | 0.025 | 0.025 | 2.45g | | |
| 30g | 0.75 | | | 0.75 | 90g |
| 2g | 0.05 | 0.05 | 4.9g | | |
| 5g | 0.125 | 0.125 | 12.25g | 0.125 | 15g |

**5.** (i) A(Fe) = 56g
(ii) M(Fe$_3$O$_4$) = 232g
(iii) M(H$_2$) = 2g

| Mass of iron used | No. of moles of iron used | No. of moles of iron oxide formed | Mass of iron oxide formed | No. of moles of hydrogen formed | Mass of hydrogen formed |
|---|---|---|---|---|---|
| 42g | 0.75 | 0.25 | 58g | | |
| 16.8g | 0.3 | 0.1 | 23.2g | | |
| 63g | 1.125 | | | 1.5 | 3g |
| 8.4g | 0.15 | 0.05 | 11.6g | | |
| 21g | 0.375 | 0.125 | 29g | 0.5 | 1.0g |

**6.** 3 750 Kg iron pyrites
6 125 Kg sulphuric acid
**7.** 0.6g magnesium left
7.35g acid
**8.** $XCl_{3(aq)} + 3AgNO_{3(aq)} \longrightarrow X(NO_3)_{3(aq)} + 3AgCl_{(s)}$
M(XCl$_3$.6H$_2$O) = 270.5
$A_r$(X) = 56
**9.** 132.5 Kg sodium carbonate
125 Kg calcium carbonate
**10.** 64.4% sodium sulphate
5.9g sodium chloride
**11.** (a) 26.76g
(b) 27.4g
**12.** (a) 2g
(b) 140g dm$^{-3}$
**13.** (a) 2.1g sodium hydrogen
carbonate
(b) 58% sodium carbonate

---

**Section D**
**1.** (a) 0.1 mole
(b) 0.15 mole
(c) 0.03 mole
(d) 0.1 mole
(e) 0.048 mole
**2.** (a) 0.5M
(b) 2.5M
(c) 6.67M
(d) 4M
(e) 1.5M
**3.** (a) 12.0g
(b) 4.0g

(c) 0.424g
(d) 0.56g
(e) 1.5g

**4.** (a) 0.25M
(b) 5.0M
(c) 0.143M
(d) 0.5M
(e) 0.8M

**5.** (a) 50 cm$^3$
(b) 40 cm$^3$
(c) 40 cm$^3$
(d) 30 cm$^3$

**6.1.** (a) $NaOH_{(aq)} + HCl_{(aq)} \longrightarrow NaCl_{(aq)} + H_2O_{(l)}$
   (i) 0.02 mole
   (ii) 0.02 mole
   (iii) 1 mol dm$^{-3}$

  (b) $H_2SO_{4(aq)} + 2KOH_{(aq)} \longrightarrow K_2SO_{4(aq)} + 2H_2O_{(l)}$
   (i) 0.02 mole
   (ii) 0.04 mole
   (iii) 1 mol dm$^{-3}$

  (c) $CaCl_{2(aq)} + 2AgNO_{3(aq)} \longrightarrow Ca(NO_3)_{2(aq)} + 2AgCl_{(s)}$
   (i) 0.075 mole
   (ii) 0.15 mole
   (iii) 5 mol dm$^{-3}$

  (d) $2HNO_{3(aq)} + Na_2CO_{3(aq)} \longrightarrow$
$$2NaNO_{3(aq)} + CO_{2(g)} + H_2O_{(l)}$$
   (i) 0.001 mole
   (ii) 0.0005 mole
   (iii) 0.02 mol dm$^{-3}$

  (e) $3H_2SO_{4(aq)} + 2X(OH)_{3(aq)} \longrightarrow X_2(SO_4)_{3(aq)} + 6H_2O_{(l)}$
   (i) 0.005 mole
   (ii) 0.0033 mole
   (iii) 0.33 mol dm$^{-3}$

**6.2.** (a) $HCl_{(aq)} + KOH_{(aq)} \longrightarrow KCl_{(aq)} + H_2O_{(l)}$
   14g dm$^{-3}$

  (b) $2HNO_{3(aq)} + Ba(OH)_{2(aq)} \longrightarrow Ba(NO_3)_{2(aq)} + 2H_2O_{(l)}$
   68.4g dm$^{-3}$

  (c) $2AgNO_{3(aq)} + MgBr_{2(aq)} \longrightarrow 2AgBr_{(s)} + Mg(NO_3)_{2(aq)}$
   23g dm$^{-3}$

  (d) $Na_2CO_{3(aq)} + 2HCl_{(aq)} \longrightarrow 2NaCl_{(aq)} + CO_{2(g)} + H_2O_{(l)}$
   14.6g dm$^{-3}$

**7.** (a) $HCl_{(aq)} + NaOH_{(aq)} \longrightarrow NaCl_{(aq)} + H_2O_{(l)}$
   (i) 0.025 mole
   (ii) 0.025 mole
   (iii) 25 cm$^3$

  (b) $2HCl_{(aq)} + Na_2CO_{3(aq)} \longrightarrow 2NaCl_{(aq)} + CO_{2(g)} + H_2O_{(l)}$
   (i) 0.04 mole
   (ii) 0.02 mole
   (iii) 20 cm$^3$

  (c) $K_2CO_{3(aq)} + H_2SO_{4(aq)} \longrightarrow K_2SO_{4(aq)} + CO_{2(g)} + H_2O_{(l)}$
   (i) 0.02 mole

        (ii) 0.02 mole

        (iii) 10 cm³

   (d) $NH_4Cl_{(aq)} + AgNO_{3(aq)} \longrightarrow NH_4NO_{3(aq)} + AgCl_{(s)}$

        (i) 0.005 mole

        (ii) 0.005 mole

        (iii) 250 cm³

   (e) $2NaOH_{(aq)} + H_2SO_{4(aq)} \longrightarrow Na_2SO_{4(aq)} + 2H_2O_{(1)}$

        (i) 0.00625 mole

        (ii) 0.003125 mole

        (iii) 25 cm³

**8.1.** (a) 0.1 mole

   (b) $M[Z(OH)_2] = 58g$

   (c) $A_r(Z) = 24$

**8.2.** (a) (i) $MO_{(s)} + 2HCl_{(aq)} \longrightarrow MCl_{2(aq)} + H_2O_{(a)}$

       (ii) 0.04 mole

       (iii) 0.02 mole

       (iv) $M(MO) = 80g$    $A_r(M) = 64$

   (b) (i) $X_2O_{3(s)} + 3H_2SO_{4(aq)} \longrightarrow X_2(SO_4)_{3(aq)} + 3H_2O_{(1)}$

       (ii) 0.01 mole

       (iii) 0.0033 mole

       (iv) $M(X_2O_3) = 102g$    $A_r(X) = 27$

   (c) (i) $A_2CO_{3(aq)} + 2HNO_{3(aq)} \longrightarrow$

                      $2ANO_{3(aq)} + CO_{2(g)} + H_2O_{(1)}$

       (ii) 0.0025 mole

       (iii) 0.00125 mole

       (iv) $M(A_2CO_3) = 232g$    $A_r(A) = 86$

**9.**    $NaCl_{(aq)} + AgNO_{3(aq)} \longrightarrow NaNO_{3(aq)} + AgCl_{(s)}$

   (a) 0.0025 mole

   (b) 0.0025 mole

   (c) 5.85 g dm⁻³

   (d) 75%

**10.1** (a) 0.06

   (b) 0.06

   (c) 0.12

   (d) 0.06

   (e) 0.6

**10.2** (a) 0.125

   (b) 0.25

   (c) 0.375

**11.** (a) 0.002 mole

   (b) 0.05 mol dm⁻³

   (c) 4.5 g

   (d) 1.8g water; $x = 2$

**12.** (a) 0.00025 mole

   (b) 0.0005 mole

      Formula = $Na_2HPO_4$

      $2NaOH_{(aq)} + H_3PO_{4(aq)} \longrightarrow Na_2HPO_{4(aq)} + 2H_2O_{(1)}$

**13.** 2:1

**14.** (a) 0.125 mol dm⁻³

   (b) 21.25g dm⁻³

   0.7175g silver chloride

15. $A_r(X) = 30$  Bromine
16. 0.025 mole excess sulphuric acid
    0.025 mole acid reacted
    $A_r(M) = 24$
17. $M(XCO_3) = 148g$
    $25 \text{ cm}^3$
18. (a) 0.01 moles sodium hydroxide formed
    23% sodium
    (b) $120 \text{ cm}^3$ hydrogen
19. (a) $66.25g \text{ dm}^{-3}$ $Na_2CO_3$
    (b) $178.75g \text{ dm}^{-3}$ $Na_2CO_3 \cdot 10H_2O$
    (c) 0.3125 mole $Na^+$
20. 0.04 mole sodium chloride formed
    Sodium hydroxide: 1.0M
    Hydrochloric acid: 1.6M
21. $X(OH)_{2(aq)} + 2HCl_{(aq)} \longrightarrow XCl_{2(aq)} + 2H_2O_{(l)}$
    0.01 mole $X(OH)_2$
    0.02 mole HCl
    0.01 mole $XCl_2$
    Ratio of 1:2:1 as in the equation
22. Emprical formula: $C_2H_3O_3$
    $M(\text{Acid}) = 150g$
    Molecular formula: $C_4H_6O_6$

---

**Section E**
1.1. (a) $300 \text{ cm}^3$
     (b) $500 \text{ cm}^3$
     (c) $810 \text{ cm}^3$
     (d) $316 \text{ cm}^3$
     (e) $400 \text{ cm}^3$
     (f) $1638 \text{ cm}^3$
     (g) $780 \text{ cm}^3$
     (h) $920 \text{ cm}^3$
1.2. 800 mm
1.3 $-33°C$
2.1. (a) $H_{2(g)} + Cl_{2(g)} \longrightarrow 2HCl_{(g)}$    $50 \text{ cm}^3$ hydrogen
     (b) $2H_{2(g)} + O_{2(g)} \longrightarrow 2H_2O_{(l)}$    $200 \text{ cm}^3$ hydrogen
     (c) $3H_{2(g)} + N_{2(g)} \longrightarrow 2NH_{3(g)}$    $75 \text{ cm}^3$ hydrogen
2.2. (a) $200 \text{ cm}^3$
     (b) $500 \text{ cm}^3$
     (c) $500 \text{ cm}^3$
3.1. $2H_{2(g)} + O_{2(g)} \longrightarrow 2H_2O_{(l)}$
     (a) $50 \text{ cm}^3$
     (b) $50 \text{ cm}^3$
     (c) $50 \text{ cm}^3$
     (d) $150 \text{ cm}^3$
3.2. $600 \text{ cm}^3$ oxygen
     (a) $400 \text{ cm}^3$ carbon dioxide

(b) 400 cm³ carbon dioxide
+ 400 cm³ steam
150 dm³ of air
20 dm³ carbon dioxide
+ 120 dm³ nitrogen

**4.1** (a) $2CO_{(g)} + O_{2(g)} \longrightarrow 2CO_{2(g)}$
Gases left: 150 cm³ carbon dioxide

(b) Equation as (a)
Gases left: 25 cm³ oxygen + 50 cm³ carbon dioxide

(c) $H_{2(g)} + Cl_{2(g)} \longrightarrow 2HCl_{(g)}$
Gases left: 120 cm³ hydrogen chloride + 20 cm³ chlorine

(d) $2H_{2(g)} + O_{2(g)} \longrightarrow 2H_2O_{(1)}$
Gases left: 20 cm³ hydrogen

(e) $N_{2(g)} + 3H_{2(g)} \longrightarrow 2NH_{3(g)}$
Gases left: 60 cm³ ammonia + 15 cm³ nitrogen

**4.2.** (a) 6.5 dm³

(b) 2 dm³

(c) 40 cm³ oxygen + 160 cm³
carbon dioxide

(d) 40 cm³ butane + 240 cm³
carbon dioxide
40 cm³ butane, 240 cm³ carbon
dioxide and 300 cm³ steam

**5.** $M_r(SO_2) = 64$
(a) 2.8 dm³
(b) 2.67 dm³

**6.** $2CO_{(g)} + O_{2(g)} \longrightarrow 2CO_{2(g)}$
$2H_{2(g)} + O_{2(g)} \longrightarrow 2H_2O_{(1)}$
2.5 dm³ oxygen

**7.** $2C_8H_{18(1)} + 25O_{2(g)} \longrightarrow 16CO_{2(g)} + 18H_2O_{(1)}$
(a) 1:2
(b) 125 dm³ air
Gases left: 100 dm³ nitrogen + 16 dm³ carbon dioxide

**8.** $C_2H_{4(g)} + 3O_{2(g)} \longrightarrow 2CO_{2(g)} + 2H_2O_{(1)}$
$2C_2H_{6(g)} + 7O_{2(g)} \longrightarrow 4CO_{2(g)} + 6H_2O_{(1)}$
325 cm³ oxygen
200 cm³ carbon dixode

**9.** (a) Nil
(b) 50 cm³ sulphur dioxide
(c) 100 cm³ hydrogen sulphide
(d) 50 cm³ steam + 25 cm³ sulphur
dioxide

**10.** $2NH_{3(g)} + 3CuO_{(s)} \longrightarrow N_{2(g)} + 3Cu_{(s)} + 3H_2O_{(1)}$
80% ammonia

**11.** 75 cm³
25 cm³ unused oxygen

**12.** (a) 300 cm³ oxygen
(b) 200 cm³ carbon dioxide
(c) $C_4H_8$
$C_4H_{8(g)} + 6O_{2(g)} \longrightarrow 4CO_{2(g)} + 4H_2O_{(1)}$

**Section F**
1.  (a) 24.2 dm$^3$
    (b) 24.4 dm$^3$
    (c) 23.2 dm$^3$
    (d) 23.8 dm$^3$
    (e) 24.4 dm$^3$
2.1. (a) 22.4 dm$^3$
    (b) 4.48 dm$^3$
    (c) 33.6 dm$^3$
    (d) 3.36 dm$^3$
    (e) 448 cm$^3$
    (f) 22.4x dm$^3$
2.2. (a) 6 dm$^3$
    (b) 76.8 dm$^3$
    (c) 480 cm$^3$
    (d) 32.4 dm$^3$
    (e) 3 dm$^3$
2.3. (a) 1
    (b) 0.1
    (c) 2.5
    (d) 0.03
    (e) x/22400
2.4 (a) $\frac{1}{12}$(0.0833)
    (b) $\frac{1}{40}$(0.025)
    (c) $\frac{1}{15}$(0.067)
    (d) 1/2000 (0.0005)
    (e) 0.012
3.  (a) 6 dm$^3$
    (b) 60 dm$^3$
    (c) 750 cm$^3$
    (d) 720 cm$^3$
    (e) 600 dm$^3$
4.  (a) 29g
    (b) 1.33g
    (c) 0.16g
    (d) 175g
    (e) 0.02g
5.  (a) 16
    (b) 42
    (c) 64
    (d) 4
6.  (a) (i) 0.15 mole
        (ii) 0.15 mole
        (iii) 3.6 dm$^3$
    (b) (i) 0.0125 mole
        (ii) 0.0125 mole
        (iii) 300 cm$^3$
    (c) (i) $\frac{1}{70}$ (0.0143) mole
        (ii) 1/140 (0.00715) mole
        (iii) 171.4 cm$^3$

(d) (i) 0.005 mole
    (ii) 0.0125 mole
    (iii) 300 $cm^3$

**7.1.** (a) 0.02 mole
  (b) 0.03 mole
  (c) 2.4g

**7.2** (a) 0.04 mole
  (b) 0.02 mole
  (c) 480 $cm^3$

**7.3.** (a) 5.5 moles
  (b) 2 moles
  (c) 240g
  96 $dm^3$ sulphur dioxide

**7.4.** (a) $\frac{1}{12}$ (0.0833) mole
  (b) $\frac{1}{16}$ (0.0625) mole
  (c) 3.5g

**8.** 6.9g ethanol

**9.** 1:2:8:16

**10.** $M_r$(gas) = 42
  $C_3H_6$

**11.** (a) 400 $cm^3$
  (b) 413.6 $cm^3$

**12.** 1.20g
  (a) 0.67g
  (b) 1.83g

**13.** (a) 25.3 $dm^3$
  (b) 22.4 $dm^3$

**14.** 112
  $C_8H_{16}$

**15.** $CH_{4(g)} + 4CuO_{(s)} \longrightarrow CO_{2(g)} + 4Cu_{(s)} + 2H_2O_{(1)}$
  Decrease = 1.6g

**16.** $2NaHCO_{3(s)} + H_2SO_{4(aq)} \longrightarrow$
                             $Na_2SO_{4(aq)} + 2CO_{2(g)} + 2H_2O_{(1)}$
  0.15 mol $dm^{-3}$

**17.** (a) 2.65g sodium carbonate
  (b) 3.575g $Na_2CO_3 \cdot 10H_2O$

**18.** $N_2H_4CO_{(s)} + 2NaOH_{(aq)} \longrightarrow 2NH_{3(g)} + Na_2CO_{3(aq)}$
  800 $cm^3$ ammonia
  13.3 $cm^3$ hydrochloric acid

**19.** $Na_2SO_{3(s)} + 2HCl_{(aq)} \longrightarrow 2NaCl_{(aq)} + SO_{2(g)} + H_2O_{(1)}$
  160 $cm^3$ sulphur dioxide at s.t.p.
  181 $cm^3$

**20.** 140 $cm^3$
  0.9125g hydrochloric acid

---

**Section G**

**1.** Simplest formula: $Sb_2S_3$
  Molecular formula: $Sb_2S_3$
  $Sb_2S_{3(s)} + 6HCl_{(aq)} \longrightarrow 2SbCl_{3(aq)} + 3H_2S_{(g)}$
  360 $cm^3$ hydrogen sulphide

2. $CaH_2$
   $CaH_{2(s)} + 2H_2O_{(l)} \longrightarrow Ca(OH)_{2(aq)} + 2H_{2(g)}$
   (a) $224 \ cm^3$
   (b) $222.93 \ cm^3$
3. $\frac{1}{40}$ mole $NaHCO_3$
   $\frac{1}{80}$ mole carbon dioxide
   $\frac{1}{80}$ mole $Na_2CO_3$
   Ratio of 2:1:1 as in the equation
   $2NaHCO_{3(s)} \longrightarrow Na_2CO_{3(s)} + CO_{2(g)} + H_2O_{(l)}$
   0.225g water
4. $Mg_3N_2$
   180g Mg + 70g N₂
   $Mg_3N_{2(s)} + 6H_2O_{(l)} \longrightarrow 3Mg(OH)_{2(s)} + 2NH_{3(g)}$
   $960 \ cm^3$ ammonia
   $20 \ cm^3$ acid solution
5. (a) 2g sulphur dioxide
   (b) 1g sulphur
   (c) $Cu_2S$
6. (a) 0.78g
   (b) $20 \ cm^3$
7. $NaH_{(s)} + H_2O_{(l)} \longrightarrow NaOH_{(aq)} + H_{2(g)}$
   (a) $4g \ dm^{-3}$
   (b) $560 \ cm^3$
8. (a) 1.68g
   (b) 54.62g
   (c) 3.25g
   (d) $1300 \ cm^3$
   (e) M(Alkene) = 56g
   $C_4H_8$
9. (a) $112 \ cm^3$
   (b) 0.005 mole hydrogen sulphide; 0.00167 mole $X_2S_3$
   (c) $M_r(X_2S_3) = 246$; $A_r(X) = 75$
10. $Mg_{(s)} + 2HCl_{(aq)} \longrightarrow MgCl_{2(aq)} + H_{2(g)}$
    (a) Expt. I
    (b) Increased
    (c) Not in expt. II
    (d) I: $224 \ cm^3$
        II: $140 \ cm^3$
    Vol. of hydrogen not doubled in (i), (ii) or (iii)
11. $CuCO_{3(s)} + 2HCl_{(aq)} \longrightarrow CuCl_{2(aq)} + CO_{2(g)} + H_2O_{(l)}$
    (a) I, II and III
    (b) III
    (c) II and IV
12. (a) 1/600 mole silver
    (b) 1/1200 mole or 0.0533g copper
    (c) 1/1200 mole hydrogen
        (i) $18.67 \ cm^3$
        (ii) $18.58 \ cm^3$
13. (a) 0.16g sulphur
    (b) 20.25% sulphur
    $x = 6$

**14.** 0.6g carbon; 0.133g hydrogen

% composition; 60% carbon, 13.33% hydrogen, 26.67% oxygen

$C_3H_8O$

**15.** Emprical formula: $CH_2$

Vol. of vapour at s.t.p. = 336 cm³

$M_r = 60$     Molec. formula: $C_2H_4O_2$

0.05 mole of each substance

$C_2H_4O_{2(s)} + NaOH_{(aq)} \longrightarrow Na^+C_2H_3O_2^-{}_{(aq)} + H_2O_{(l)}$

Monobasic

**16.** (a) 35% nitrogen

(b) 20% impurities

(c) $NH_4NO_{3(s)} + NaOH_{(aq)} \longrightarrow$

$$NaNO_{3(aq)} + NH_{3(g)} + H_2O_{(l)}$$

0.4g sodium hydroxide

(d) 224 cm³, (e) 243.2 cm³ ammonia

**17.** Empirical formula: $NO_2$

M(Oxide) = 92     Molec. formula: $N_2O_4$

$N_2O_{4(g)} + 2NaOH_{(aq)} \longrightarrow$

$$NaNO_{3(aq)} + NaNO_{2(aq)} + H_2O_{(l)}$$

40 cm³ sodium hydroxide solution

**18.** (a) $Fe_3O_4$

(b) $Fe_2O_3$

(c) 2400 dm³

**19.** (a) Empirical formula: $C_7H_{16}$

(b) $M_r = 100$     Molec. formula: $C_7H_{16}$

(c) 6 000 dm³ vapour

(d) $C_7H_{16(g)} + 11O_{2(g)} \longrightarrow 7CO_{2(g)} + 8H_2O_{(l)}$

66 000 dm³ oxygen

(e) 330 000 dm³ air

Gases left: 42 000 dm³ carbon dioxide + 264 000 dm³ nitrogen

**20.** (a) 0.04 mole hydrogen chloride

$M(XCl_2) = 111g$     $A_r(X) = 40$

(b) 0.0033 mole $XCl_2$     0.0133 mole ammonia

$y = 4$